AFRICAN CICHLIDS II: CICHLIDS FROM EAST AFRICA

Wolfgang Staeck · Horst Linke

Wolfgang Staeck · Horst Linke

AFRICAN CICHLIDS II

CICHLIDS FROM EAST AFRICA

A handbook for their
identification, care
and breeding

Cover photographs:
Above left: *Paracyprichromis nigripinnis* from Lake Tanganyika

Above right: *Tropheus* sp. "Bemba" from Lake Tanganyika

Below left: *Aulonocara stuartgranti* from Lake Malawi

Below right: *Pseudotropheus* sp. "zebra tangerine" from Lake Malawi

Photo insertion front: Rocky littoral with species of *Neolamprologus* on Cape Chaitika (Zambia) in the southern Lake Tanganyika

Photo insertion rear: *Mbuna*-cichlids in an underwater reef off the Likoma Island in Lake Malawi

Rear cover photograph: *Julidochromis ornatus* from Lake Tanganyika (Photo: H. Linke)

The African Cichlids are presented in 2 volumes:

Cichlids I: Cichlids from West Africa
Cichlids II: Cichlids from East Africa

© 1994 Tetra-Press
Tetra-Werke Dr. rer nat. Ulrich Baensch GmbH
Herrenteich 78, D-49324 Melle, Germany

Distributed in U.S.A. by
Tetra Sales U.S.A.
3001 Commerce Street
Blacksburg, VA 24060

Distributed in UK by
Tetra Sales, Lambert Court,
Chestnut Avenue, Eastleigh Hampshire S05 3ZQ

Translation from German: HERPRINT INTERNATIONAL cc,
P.O. Box 14117, Bredell 1623, South Africa

Typesetting: Fotosatz Hoffmann, Hennef

Printed in Germany

WL-Code 16756
ISBN 1-56465-167-3

CONTENTS

PREFACE

This book is a translation of the completely revised, updated, and expanded 1993 edition of the volume which was originally published in 1981. A comparison with the original edition shows that our view of the cladistic relationships and the evolution of the Cichlids inhabiting the East African lakes has considerably changed. This obviously has had an impact on the systematics and the taxonomy and has led to a great number of changes regarding the scientific names of the individual species. The systematics of a large number of Cichlids from Lake Malawi and the Tanganyika-cichlids especially were subjected to radical revisions during the decade which has passed since the first edition was published. The taxonomy of the Cichlids inhabiting Lake Victoria has also changed. One of the results of all these revisions is that ten new genera have been established for the Tanganyika-cichlids and twenty for the Malawi-cichlids. This enormous growth of knowledge is not only reflected by the numerous new species discovered or taxonomically dealt with for the first time, but also the large number of species which have been imported alive for the first time.

The chapter "Register of commonly used Synonyms" in the appendix on page 194 lists all names commonly used by aquarists in the past and the respective new scientific ones. By using this list, finding a particular species in the book should not be a problem.

Our sincere thanks are due to Norman J. EDWARDS (Blantyre), Misha FAINZILBER (Dar-es-Salaam), and Stuart GRANT (Salima), without whose assistance in Africa this book could have never been completed. For the mediation of photographs or information we are indebted to Heidemarie SCHREIBER, Erwin SCHRAML, and Lothar SEEGERS.

Berlin / Schwarzenbach am Wald 1993   Wolfgang Staeck   Horst Linke

CICHLIDS FROM EAST AFRICA

East Africa in a restricted sense means the area occupied by the countries Uganda, Kenya, and Tanzania which are all border-countries of Lake Victoria. In a wider sense, the countries bordering Lake Malawi or which lie on the eastern shore of Lake Tanganyika are also included. These are the countries of Burundi, Zambia, Malawi, and Mozambique.

The zoogeography, i.e. the science dealing with the occurrence and distribution of animals on earth, uses the term Faunal Regions to refer to areas which have a homogenous fauna. Equally, ichthyologists use the term Fish Region to consolidate water-bodies which approximately hold the same species of fishes and can thus be distinguished from others.

The portion of the African continent which is generally referred to as East Africa is in no way a region with a homogenous ichthyofauna. According to POLL it covers no less than four different Fish Regions. The largest of these regions, which on the other hand holds a comparatively small number of species, has been given the name East African Fish Region. As can be perceived from the map, it includes the countries Mozambique, Tanzania, Kenya, Somalia, and Ethiopia. Although this book deals with the Cichlids of East Africa, this region is of no great importance since its typical representa-

East African Cichlids often have bright, striking colours. Male of *Labeotropheus trewavasae* from the littoral of the island of Thumbi West.

tives have only found their way into the aquaria of the Cichlid-enthusiasts by exception. The remaining three fish regions of East Africa have been named Lake Victoria, Lake Tanganyika, and Lake Malawi. They play a major role for the aquarist and, in the following, the latter two mentioned are especially given priority and are dealt with in more detail.

According to our knowledge today it appears likely that there are far more than 1500 species of Cichlids living on earth of which approximately a quarter has not even been scientifically described. More than half of all Cichlid-species has its distribution in East Africa. On account of this fact, two different concepts had to be chosen for the two volumes on African Cichlids. Whilst it was tried to portray the Cichlids of the West African fish regions as complete as possible in the first volume, this second volume can only take a couple of representative species into consideration. The following selection criteria have been applied. Firstly those Cichlids which are interesting and recommendable for the aquarist should be portrayed, but, on the other hand, a representative overview of the diversity of forms and ecologies in these fish regions should also be given. The pre-defined volume of this book obviously determined to what extent this was possible.

Many East African Cichlids have already been known to ichthyology since the end of the last century. The majority was discovered by Englishmen who usually donated their collections to the British Museum in London. There, the fishes were scientifically examined and described by the Belgian ichthyologist BOULENGER. Some of today's most popular aquarium fishes were already amongst the Cichlids collected by MOORE during a journey to Lake Tanganyika in 1895/96. Further important information was also gathered by the Belgian hydrobiological expedition during the years 1946/47 whose results were published by POLL. The first Malawi-cichlids were collected by KIRK as early as 1861 when he accompanied LIVINGSTONE on his expeditions. These species were described by GÜNTHER in 1864. Besides other Englishmen, the German FÜLLEBORN caught new species of Cichlids in Lake Malawi in 1900/1901 which were subsequently described by AHL (1927). The next important collecting trip was done by WOOD in 1920. His specimens were dealt with by REGAN (1921). By order of the British Museum, CHRISTY eventually undertook a journey to Lake Malawi in 1925/26 during which 3500 Cichlids were caught and preserved. They were scientifically dealt with by the ichthyologist TREWAVAS. The result was numerous new species whose names were published for the first time in 1935. The first synoptic description of the Victoria-cichlids was authored by REGAN and appeared in 1922.

Out of the four East African fish regions, Lake Victoria is probably the one with the most Cichlids. Experts estimate that it is inhabited by far more than 200 different species of which only half have been described. It is interesting that these fishes generally have a more homogenous appearance in comparison with those from the other two East African Lakes. This phenomenon led to the fact that most Victorian cichlids were originally described as species of *Haplochromis*. Recent comparative genetic studies (MEYER et al. 1990) have revealed that these Cichlids have an unexpected low degree of genetic variability and must therefore be considered to be of monophyletic origin, which means they all have the same ancestor. This is the reason why the genera introduced by GREENWOOD have been synonymized, and the Victoria-cichlids are today again referred to as *Haplochromis*.

In contrast to the Cichlids of the other two great East African lakes, the species of Lake Victoria have rarely been imported for the ornamental fish trade. Whilst certain Malawi- and Tanganyika-cichlids belong to the standard range of species available, Victoria-cichlids have only been kept by a few extreme Cichlid-enthusiasts who have specialized in the study of rare species. None of these species has ever achieved to become really popular and widespread amongst aquarists. This is the reason why the Cichlids of Lake Victoria could not be given more attention in this book.

Without a single exception, all Cichlids in Lake Victoria are mouthbrooders. Amongst them are numerous species whose males are particularly attractive, and their colourations can easily compete with certain Malawi-cichlids. Unfortunately the males show these colours only when they have occupied a territory and during courtship. Under the mostly insufficient keeping conditions of the fish-trade their attractive colours can barely be imagined.

For the aquarist it is furthermore of importance to know that many species of Lake Victoria closely resemble each other. Whereas mature males may still be easily distinguished due to their splendid and specific colourations, the females are without exception drab and in many cases look almost the same. In praxis it is therefore extremely difficult to allocate the correct females to the male specimens. Even the specific identification of preserved specimens is difficult in many cases and in the case of a live fish it is often impossible.

From Lake Malawi, more than 400 species of Cichlids have been described to date which are assigned to approximately 50 genera. It is however certain that the number of Cichlids inhabiting these waters is much higher. Recent estimates indicate that the real number of species may even exceed the five-hundred mark. Approximately 120 of the Malawi-cichlids were initially allocated to the compilationgenus *Haplochromis* until the British ichthyologists ECCLES and TREWAVAS (1989) completely revised this group

The number of species and individuals in the rocky littoral of Lake Malawi is surprising. At least seven different Mbuna-cichlids can be identified in the photograph. Littoral of the island of Thumbi West at four metres depth.

of affiliated species. The result of their investigations was a division of the Lake Malawi-*Haplochromis* into 23 new genera. This has also had an influence on many species of popular aquarium fishes which since carry a new generic name.

Amongst the Haplochromines, especially the so-called Mbuna-cichlids have achieved a rank of great importance for the aquarists. This name has been adopted from African fisherman and comprises a group of Cichlids whose distribution is strictly limited to the rocky and rubble zones where they find their vegetarian food. A few species also occur in the transitory zone to the sandy littoral. Altogether, the Mbuna-cichlids belong to more than fifty species which are allocated to eleven genera. This number constantly increases since the group contains a couple of Cichlids which have not been scientifically described, but which have partly already become popular amongst aquarists.

Other important aquarium fishes are found amongst the so-called Utaka-cichlids. This name also originates from African languages and refers to a group of Cichlids which migrate to the shores during the breeding season, but otherwise have a pelagic ecology, i.e. inhabit the open waters where they primarily feed on zooplankton. These Cichlids with their marvellous males in usually blue colourations are assigned to the genus *Copadichromis*. For the aquaristic praxis it is useful to know that almost all species of Malawi-cichlids are mouthbrooders. The only two exceptions in these waters are two species of *Tilapia* which are substratum-spawners.

Almost 200 different species of Cichlids have been described from Lake Tanganyika. This number is also on the increase as can be predicted from the number of new discoveries made during the past few years. Large parts of the shores on Tanzanian and Zaïrian territory have not yet been explored in detail.

The Tanganyika-cichlids are assigned to 55 genera. The most important one of them is *Neolamprologus* which presently incorporates 52 species and subspecies.

Lake Tanganyika assumes a separate position in so far that it — in contrast to Lakes Malawi and Victoria in which mouthbrooders clearly dominate — also has a few substratum-brooders and a larger group of cavebrooders. Altogether, these are approximately 70 species which belong to the six genera *Neolamprologus*, *Lepidolamprologus*, *Altolamprologus*, *Julidochromis*, *Chalinochromis*, and *Telmatochromis*.

The habitats of the Cichlids inhabiting the three great East African Lakes differ considerably from the biotopes of their West African relatives which have been dealt with in detail in Volume I. The most important Cichlid-biotopes in West Africa are rivers and streams of the tropical rainforest. In addition to these, water-bodies in the savannas are also inhabited. In East Africa on the other side, it is the three large lakes in which Cichlids are caught for the hobby. On account of their enormous sizes, these water-bodies do not fit into the picture one usually has in mind for an inland lake. Lake Victoria covers an area of just under 70 000 square kilometres and is between three- and four-hundred kilometres broad. Lake Tanganyika measures almost seven-hundred kilometres in length and maximally eighty in width, and Lake Malawi is six-hundred kilometres long with a breadth of up to eighty-seven kilometres. Due to their immense sizes, the predominant conditions can in all three cases easily be compared with e.g. the Baltic Sea. A moderate breeze may already lead to strong waves, and a storm results in an enormous well which only sea-worthy boats can cope with. The greatest depth is indicated as 1470 metres for Lake Tanganyika and 758 metres for Lake Malawi respectively. In comparison with these figures, Lake Victoria is rather shallow with its greatest depth being only ninety metres. The surface temperature of all three lakes varies between 24 and 29 °C. In Lake Malawi especially, there are very pronounced and regular changes of the tem-

A typical biotope of West African Cichlids. White flowers of the Hooked Lily, *Crinum natans*, emerge from the brown water of a rainforest stream.

The species of *Pelvicachromis* rank amongst the most popular West African Cichlids. The red variety of *P. pulcher* is particularly splendid.

perature which correspond with the seasonal changes. At greater depths, the water-temperature decreases to a minimum of 22 °C in Lake Malawi and to 23 °C in Lake Tanganyika. In both lakes, depths are free of fishes since the water there does not contain oxygen. The border at which fishes may still live is not exactly known, but should generally be situated between one- and twohundred metres.

Table 1
Important water-values of Lake Malawi

Lake Malawi	
Clarity:	up to 20 m
pH:	7,7 − 8,6
Total hardness:	4 − 6 °dH
Carbonate hardness:	6 − 8 °dH
Conductivity at 20 °C:	210 − 285 micro-Siemens/cm
Surface temperature:	24 − 29 °C
Deep-level temp.:	22 °C

Regarding its chemical and physical features, the water of the three big East African lakes distinctly differs from the water-bodies inhabited by Cichlids in West Africa. The most important consequence of this fact for the aquaristic practice is that East African Cichlids are much easier to breed in captivity than their West African relatives from the tropical rainforests. In general, the water of all three large lakes is distinctly alkaline. It furthermore contains many dissolved minerals and is therefore of a certain hardness. In summary it thus largely resembles the water found in most regions of central Europe.

Furthermore, it is significant for the aquaristic praxis that both Lake Malawi and Lake Tanganyika are extremely clear and allow sight for up to twenty metres under favourable conditions. It is therefore possible to observe and even photograph Cichlids in their natural environments in both lakes. As far as clarity is concerned, the conditions in Lake Victoria are less favourable as its water is much richer in nutrients. Only far from the shores and under extremely beneficial conditions one may

THE FISH REGIONS OF AFRICA 7—10

(after POLL 1957)

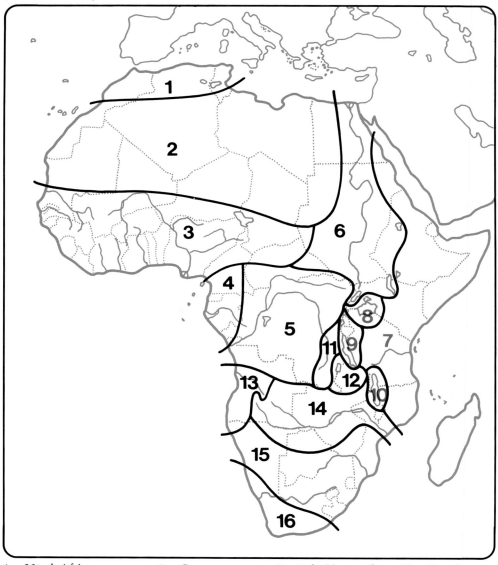

1 = North Africa	5 = Congo	9 = Lake Tanganyika	13 = Angola
2 = Sahara	6 = Nile	10 = Lake Malawi	14 = Zambezi
3 = West Africa	7 = East Africa	11 = Lualaba	15 = South Africa
4 = Cameroon and Gaboon	8 = Lake Victoria	12 = Luapula	16 = Cape Region

The first volume covers the regions 3 to 5, the second one 7 to 10

have a sight of eight metres. Normally it is restricted to one and a half to three metres due to the abundance of algae and suspended material.

Table 2
Clarity in East African Lakes

Lake Tanganyika	up to 22 m
Lake Malawi	up to 20 m
Lake Victoria	up to 8 m

Every water-body has a number of food sources for Cichlids as well as suitable places to spawn and to rear the fry. Out of the multitude of possible combinations, each species uses only a small portion that is typical for this particular fish and thus occupies, as ecologists formulate it, a certain ecological niche. Due to the fact that relatively few species inhabit similarly structured niches, the interspecific competition with regard to food, spawning sites, and hiding-places is greatly reduced. This is the only reason why several species can live together in harmony in the same area.

Factors of the unanimated environment which determine the existence of fishes are such as temperature, currents, and the chemical and physical particulars of the water as well as the structure and composition of the banks and ground. On the other hand, factors of the animated environment are algae, aquatic plants, and animals which also inhabit the water and can either be classified as source of food, competitors for food, or potential predators. The confusing number of possible combinations of major environmental determinants at first glance however becomes slightly more manageable if one realizes that certain typical habitats occur frequently and can be distinguished from others. They consist of characteristic combinations of factors and are inhabited by a typical fauna.

As soon as the ecological niche occupied by a particular species has been determined,

a short glance at the composition and structure of the ground and the banks is mostly sufficient to ascertain whether the occurrence of this species can be expected here or not. Due to the highly specialized biology of feeding, breeding, and parental care which are adaptions to a certain composition of the ground, the type of ground is one of the most important determinants which influence the distribution of Cichlids in the East African lakes. In the following, the major types of biotopes are briefly portrayed.

The Cichlids kept in aquaria almost exclusively originate from the littoral, i.e. the zone along the shores. Depending on the structure of the ground, these can be identified as rubble-, rocky, or sandy littorals. The distribution of many Cichlids is only restricted to either of these biotope-types. Areas of the East African lakes with rocky ground are the preferred habitats for many fishes. The surface of the rocks is overgrown by a short mostly yellowish lawn of algae especially in the zone of shallow water near the shores. They form the major source of food for the Cichlids. The majority of aquariumfishes originate from these habitats.

Table 3
Important water-values of Lake Tanganyika

Lake Tanganyika	
Clarity:	up to 22 m
pH:	8,6 — 9,5
Total hardness:	17 — 11 °dH
Carbonate hardness:	16 — 19 °dH
Conductivity at 20 °C:	570 — 640 micro-Siemens/cm
Surface temperature:	24 — 29 °C
Deep-level temp.:	23 °C

In Lake Tanganyika as well as in Lake Malawi, the rubble-zone may hold a surprisingly high number of individuals and

Rocky zone on the southwestern shore of Lake Malawi (Cape Maclear)

variety of species. Sometimes a diver may feel as if he is in a well furnished aquarium. This biotope is characterized by a ground which is densely covered by stones and rubble. Between the fist- to football-sized stones, there are many crevices and small caves which provide shelter for the fishes living here. Usually this ecological zone covers the first ten to twenty metres off the shore and extends up to a depth of one and a half to two metres. Typical inhabitants are the Goby Cichlids in Lake Tanganyika and some species of *Labidochromis* in Lake Malawi.

The second important biotope with a rocky ground is the rocky littoral. This ecological zone is often formed as a steep bank. In its typical form it ranges over a depth of two to twenty metres. The shallow water zone is mostly absent and the depth rapidly increases from two metres to greater depths. In this ecosystem, the ground is covered with large to very large boulders between which there are relatively few but large crevices and caves. Typical Cichlids of these biotopes are some species of *Trematocranus* in Lake Malawi, *Tropheus duboisi* in Lake Tanganyika, and *Haplochromis nigricans* in Lake Victoria.

In contrast to the diversity of colours, shapes, and species which can be observed above rocky ground, areas of sandy ground appear to be strangely monotonous. Although the number of individuals may also be considerable, the number of present species is clearly lower. Whilst Cichlids from rocky grounds usually live in solitude or pairs, those of the sandy littoral often occur in schools. They usually find their food by chewing through the sand and sieving out what can be eaten.

Even amongst the sandy littorals various biotopes can be distinguished. The most important one to mention is the sandy zone in restricted sense. It is characterized by fine whitish or reddish sand in which single stones may occasionally be embedded. Typical Cichlids of this type of biotope are the species of *Lethrinops* and other Haplo-chromines in Lake Malawi and the species of *Xenotilapia* in Lake Tanganyika. Most inhabitants of the sandy ground lack dark colours. They are usually colourless whitish or grey fishes which have a silvery, but sometimes also a splendid green or blue metallic gleam on the flanks.

Further biotopes with sandy ground are the thatch-zone and dense thickets of aquatic plants which sometimes resemble marine sea-weed stretches. The latter may consist of quite a variety of plants, the predominant ones being Vallisnerias, *Cerato-phyllum, Myriophyllum* and dense thickets of *Potamogeton*. Typical inhabitants of the plant-zone are *Limnotilapia dardennii* in Lake Tanganyika and *Hemitilapia oxyrhyn-chus* in Lake Malawi.

Even the transitory zone from sandy to rocky ground represents a separate type of habitat inhabited by a typical fauna. Cichlids of this biotope are *Pseudotropheus lucerna* and certain representatives of the *Pseudotro-pheus tropheops*-group in Lake Malawi and *Neolamprologus tetracanthus* in Lake Tanganyika.

Another biotope, from which only few aquarium fishes originate, is the zone of free water. Amongst the fishes of this habitat known to the aquarists are the species of *Bathybates* from Lake Tanganyika and the species of *Copadichromis* from Lake Malawi which are comprised under the term Utaka-cichlids.

For completeness sake, the deep-water zone and the mouthing areas of larger rivers must be mentioned as biotopes for Cichlids. The latter mentioned habitat hardly plays any role for the aquaristic since almost no fishes are caught there for the purpose of export. The importance of the profundal — the zone of deep water below the littoral — for the aquaristic on the other hand is much higher. From Lake Tanganyika especially, several species of, amongst others, the genera *Benthochromis, Paracyprichromis,* and *Cyphotilapia* are kept in aquaria. They occur in depths greater than 30 metres.

THE SUITABLE TANK
FOR EAST AFRICAN CICHLIDS

The successful husbandry of Cichlids in an aquarium requires their biological needs to be fulfilled as optimally as possible. To keep fishes in good health over a longer period or even breed them in captivity necessitates a detailed knowledge of their natural biotopes and a close emulation of this environment.

Realizing this, aquarists in the past even attempted to create aquaria that would function with almost no interference of man and thus would be a closed self-regulating system. Such attempts are always destined to fail since an aquarium is an artificial habitat which necessarily differs in many aspects from a natural water-body. Furthermore it is often overlooked that even a stationary water-body in nature is no completely separated self-regulating system. Certain elements are constantly added and others are lost and it is thus bound in a permanent exchange of energy and elements with its surrounding.

For example, since there is no wind in our aquaria which would create waves and thus could enable an exchange of gases, a movement of the water surface must be arranged by an artificial aeration-pump or a filter in order to furnish the water with oxygen. In addition to this, it cannot be avoided to illuminate the aquarium, to heat it, to feed the fishes, and to exchange the water every now and then to remove metabolism end-products.

Ecologists, who study the multilateral effects between organisms and their environment, distinguish between highly adaptable organisms which are fairly tolerant towards changes in their environment and species which depend on certain conditions and have a narrow tolerance zone. The latter feel only at ease if most of the environmental factors are precisely as they are supposed to be. This group comprises the so-called problematic fishes which are difficult to keep in an aquarium and even more difficult to breed.

They usually require more than the knowledge about their temperature, light-, and food-requirements. Experienced aquarists know that water does of course not always equal water, but that its chemical make-up, i.e. its alkaline or acidic features (pH-value) and the amount and combination of dissolved elements, represents a major environmental factor.

These problems are constantly discussed in the aquaristic literature. However, even aquarists with decades of experience some-

Emulation of the rubble-zone with *Bolbitis heudelotii* and *Anubias nana*.

Emulation of the rocky littoral with *Microsorium pteropus* and *Anubias nana*.

times overlook that not only the mentioned determinants are important points to take into consideration, but that the set-up and the decoration of a tank also contain important environmental factors which have an impact on whether a fish feels at ease or not. Some species disappoint their keepers because they will not show the expected bright colours, but look dull and inconspicuous. This may have the reason that the substrate and the decoration is coloured in too dark tones and that the fishes adapt their colours to this environment. Others may permanently assume a pale and drab appearance due to the fact that the aquarium substrate consists of white gravel whereas in nature they occur in shaded rainforest streams with a dark ground.

Generally, the successful long-term husbandry of East African Cichlids requires aquaria which measure at least one and a half metres in length. One therefore needs much larger tanks than for the keeping of their West African relatives. Although there are Cichlids especially from Lake Tanganyika which can be kept and even bred in much smaller aquaria — this is explicitly pointed out in the following — but even in their case the rule applies that the tank should be as spacious as possible. In comparison with small aquaria large ones have the advantage that the husbandry of fishes generally becomes easier and that fishes behave more naturally the larger the available space is.

The fact that the husbandry of East African Cichlids necessitates larger aquaria than for the keeping of West African species is not due to a larger size. Most of them also belong to the moderately sized fishes. The larger space-requirements of the East Africans must rather be explained by the fact that, with a few exceptions, these Cichlids cannot be kept in pairs. This especially applies to the majority of mouthbrooders. Within this group of Cichlids, no bonding develops between male and female. The male specimens are constantly in a breeding mood and will engage in courtship with any conspecific female coming past. Since they generally tolerate only females ready to spawn in their territories, they permanently harass females which have difficulties to avoid the male in the limited space conditions of an aquarium. The males must therefore always be kept with a small harem.

In addition to this, it need to be taken into consideration that most of the East African Cichlids have a high degree of intraspecific aggression. Males as well as females are often highly antisocial and quarrelsome. The smaller the aquarium is, the more this factor becomes disturbing.

The intraspecific aggression of these fishes can be reduced by three means and be brought to an acceptable measure. Firstly, the tank must be sized in such a way that the individuals can avoid each other. Secondly, these species should not be kept on their own, but together with others in a community aquarium. The presence of other fishes distracts them from their conspecifics and clearly reduces the frequency of aggressive actions. A community tank for Cichlids from East Africa may have a fairly dense population since the biology of these species take into consideration that the environment must be shared with many other fishes. Some of the underwater photographs give an impression of how densely populated the biotopes of the Cichlids are.

When choosing the species for a community tank, one should pay attention to whether these also occur together in the natural habitats. This usually guarantees a harmonic co-existence in the aquarium.

In some cases it has turned out to be beneficial to keep species from completely different biotopes together in the same aquarium. For example, species of *Cyprichromis* are inhabitants of the freewater zone and thus preferably reside in the upper half of a tank and even spawn in the free water and can thus easily be kept together with pronounced ground-dwellers of the rubble-zone. On the other hand it is not advisable to socialize species from different fish regions in the same tank, e.g. those from Lake Tanganyika with others from

Lake Victoria, even if they originate from comparable ecological zones. Representatives of other families are also hardly ever suitable co-inhabitants of such aquaria. The only exceptions may be certain catfishes of the South American genera *Ancistrus, Hemiancistrus,* and *Plecostomus.*

The third method to reduce the intraspecific aggression of these Cichlids is to emulate the natural environment as closely as possible. Ninety percent of the popular East African Cichlids commonly kept by aquarists originate from the rubble- and rocky littoral of Lakes Malawi and Tanganyika. The predominant feature of these habitats is a high number of crevices, niches, and caves of different sizes which are used by the native fishes to hide, spawn, rear their juveniles, and to define the frontiers of their territories. Cichlids from these biotopes obviously only feel at ease when their aquaria also contain rocks and crevices since their mode of feeding and the entire reproductive and social behaviour is focused on the presence of a rocky environment. Caves serve as sanctuaries for subordinate specimens subjected to permanent pursuit by dominant conspecifics and offer safe hiding-places for juveniles.

Accordingly, a natural aquarium requires many rocks and stones. Since the East African lakes have water of a relatively hard quality, even rocks with a calcium-content are suitable whereas these would be harmful in a tank for West African Cichlids. On the other hand, the "hole-stones" of the Mediterranean are not really recommendable as they consume a lot of space, and even the best arrangement provides only a few caves the fishes can use.

In the aquarium, the rocks are piled up on the rear and side walls up to just under the water surface because most of the Cichlids use the upper half of the tank only if it provides hiding-places. As the majority of Cichlids lives in the vicinity of the ground, the bottom of the tank is the most important region. It should be structured with rock constructions which provide covered sec-

tions and enable the fishes to define clear borders of several territories. Furthermore, attention must be paid to the availability of small and tiny caves near the ground which may provide safe sanctuaries for the juveniles. Finally, it should not be overlooked that many Cichlids dig in the ground. All rock constructions therefore need to be anchored as firm as possible so that the digging activities of the fishes cannot lead to their collapse.

Wood, especially pieces of bog-oak, which are an important decoration item for aquaria with West African Cichlids on the other hand appears inadequate for a model of the rubble- or rocky zone. Firstly, it could increase the acidity of the water if it has been insufficiently rinsed. Secondly, it will soon give the water a yellowish colour that affects the bright blue colours which make many fishes of Lake Malawi so attractive.

The question of how a Tanganyika- or Malawi-aquarium should be decorated is partially discussed with great controversy. As can be perceived from the underwater photographs, there are biotopes in all East African lakes which are rich in aquatic flora, although the rocky and rubble-zones lack any higher aquatic plants. The only plants existing there are tiny algae which are the most important contributors to the carpet covering stones and rocks.

Purists therefore are of the opinion that plants are misplaced in a re-construction of the rubble- or rocky littoral. On the other hand, a greened aquarium can gain considerably on aesthetic attraction. In addition to this, dense plant-groups provide safe and frequently used places of safety not only for juveniles.

In general, there are no objections to the utilization of plants. It must be ensured that they do not inhibit the vital requirements of the fishes kept. Many East African Cichlids are active and skilled swimmers which definitely require sufficient space for swimming. In most aquaria, this space is however already drastically limited by the rock constructions and it would not make sense to further reduce it by a dense vegetation. This is the reason why tall-growing plants are not really adequate for such aquaria. A tank, in which it is undertaken to re-create the rocky or rubble-zone, should therefore be planted so sparsely that the free swimming space is not affected by the plants. For its decoration, plants which grow their leaves closely over the ground, e.g. *Cryptocoryne nevillii* or similar representatives of this genus, should be given preference. Water plants which do not depend on substrate, but anchor themselves directly on the rocks are also highly recommendable. These plants include the ferns *Microsorum pteropus* and *Bolbitis heudelotii* as well as the West African species of *Anubias*. *Anubias nana* is especially suited for this purpose since it grows very low. A dense thicket of these plants is an extremely efficient cover for juveniles and is readily accepted as replacement of a rubble-field. By means of the mentioned plant-species a greening of the rock constructions becomes possible which does not only follow a biological purpose but also increases the aesthetic value of a tank.

The composition of the substrate is only of special importance if the Cichlids kept originate from the sandy zone. The inhabitants of this type of biotope would not feel comfortable above gravel since several of their instinctive activities are made impossible or at least become difficult. This especially applies to the mode of feeding and the creation of spawning pits. An aquarium which is to house Cichlids from the sandy littoral should therefore exclusively be furnished with either sand or very fine gravel as substrate. Cichlids from the rubble- or rocky zones on the other hand generally do not care about what substrate is made available even though one point requires to be observed. As the underwater photographs indicate, the ground of the natural habitats of these Cichlids is usually of remarkably light colour. In contrast to their West African relatives from the tropical rainforests

which prefer dimmed light and a dark ground, the Cichlids from the littorals of Lake Malawi and Tanganyika feel at home above light ground. The bottom of the aquarium should therefore be covered with whitish or light grey sand and gravel. In very dark aquaria some species loose their bright colourations since they attempt to blend into their environment.

The most important differences between the basic requirements of West and East African Cichlids are found with regard to the chemistry of the water. Whilst the water-courses of the tropical rainforests carry very acidic water whose pH-value partly ranges in the extremely acidic zones, the water of the East African lakes is moderately hard to hard and is clearly alkaline. East African Cichlids can therefore neither be kept in water with a pH in the acidic zone nor in soft water poor in minerals since these conditions would definitely harm the fishes.

The temperature of the aquarium-water should not lie outside the range between 22 and 29 °C. For breeding attempts it is recommendable to choose a value near the top border since higher temperatures speed up the development of eggs and larvae and thus shorten the period from spawning until the juveniles swim freely.

Typical for the large East African lakes and Lakes Tanganyika and Malawi especially is the unusual clarity of the water. This

The line-ferry is sometimes also used for the transport of Malawi-cichlids.

clarity is obviously an indication of the cleanliness. It is therefore no surprise that certain Cichlids from these large lakes are sensitive to pollution of their water. This necessitates the aquarium to be connected to an efficient powerful filter-system which guarantees a mechanical clean-up of the water at all times. Even more important is a regular exchange of the water during which the invisible but notwithstanding harmful metabolism end-products of the fishes are removed. The attentive care of the water is so meaningful because a community tank with East African Cichlids usually has a relatively dense population. On account of the aforesaid, a regular exchange of a third to half of the aquarium-water with fresh water should become a standard. In the case of a smaller tank in conjunction with a dense fish-population this interval may even be shorter.

As the modern technology which reliably keeps the naturally decorated aquarium running without great additional effort has already been discussed in detail in Volume I, it need not be repeated here again. However, to complete this chapter a remark should be made regarding the choice of illumination. The range of lighting-tubes offers a variety of light-colours which are basically distinguished by those with a high content of yellow and others with a high content of blue light. The males of many Malawi-cichlids display fantastic blue colours whose brightness will be diminished by yellowish light. It is obvious that lighting-tubes with a high content of blue, i.e. the so-called daylight types, are recommended for an aquarium in which these splendid Cichlids are housed.

Provided with sufficient quantities of a varying diet and paying attention to the factors discussed above, it should, as many years of experience by the authors show, not be a problem to breed East African Cichlids in a naturally decorated aquarium and to keep them healthy in the long run. In an aquarium whose decoration comes near the conditions provided in the natural habitat it becomes unnecessary to take the eggs, larvae, or juveniles away from the Cichlids since the young fish have a fair chance to survive if the set-up of the tank is biologically correct. The underwater photographs of the natural biotopes of the Cichlids contain a variety of ideas for a purposeful and simultaneously attractive decoration of the aquarium.

Table 4
The higher the amount of dissolved minerals the higher the conductivity

Electrical conductivity at 20 °C	
Lake Tanganyika:	570—640 micro-Siemens
Lake Malawi:	210—285 micro-Siemens
Lake Victoria:	90—145 micro-Siemens

Table 5
Values above pH 7 indicate an alkaline reaction

pH-value	
Lake Tanganyika:	8,6—9,5
Lake Malawi:	7,7—8,6
Lake Victoria:	7,1—9,0

THE EAST AFRICAN LAKES

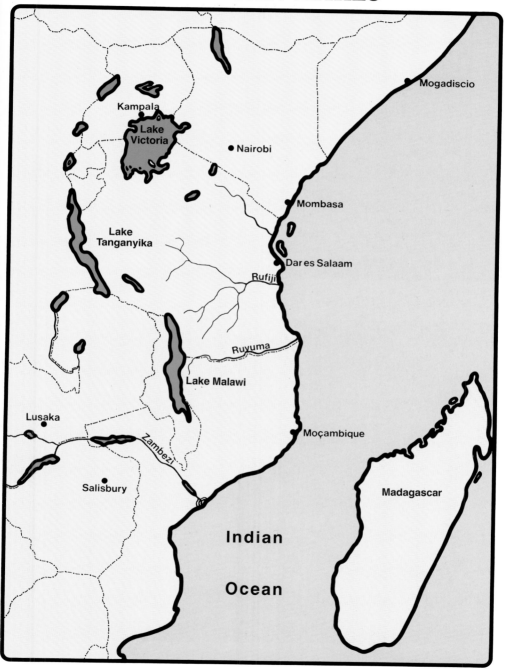

The Genus Altolamprologus
POLL, 1986

This genus presently consolidates only the two species *A. calvus* and *A. compressiceps*. Another species has meanwhile been discovered in Zambia which is yet to be described.

▶ Altolamprologus compressiceps
(BOULENGER, 1898)

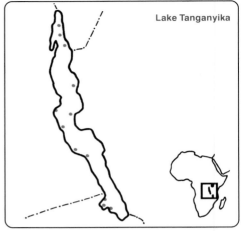

Lake Tanganyika

Localities of *Altolamprologus compressiceps*

undoubtedly belongs to the most impressive fishes of Lake Tanganyika. The pointed head, the high-backed, laterally considerably compressed body, and the high dorsal fin give this fish a unique appearance.

Exceptionally large specimens may reach a maximum length of just under thirteen centimetres. They are monomorphous, i.e. males and females look the same. Distin-guishing between the sexes is therefore extremely difficult. The dorsal and anal fins and especially the ventral fins are however slightly larger in old males than in females of comparable size. *Altolamprologus compressiceps* has developed several races with

Altolamprologus compressiceps

different body-colourations. Depending on where a specimen was caught, it may be brownish beige, curryyellow, beige brown, or olive green. The pectoral fins are chromeyellow to reddish orange. Young specimens display six to seven dark transversal stripes on the flanks which often appear as double stripes on the anterior body.

The

natural habitat

of this Cichlid is the rubble- and rocky littoral up to a depth of approximately thirty metres. They are most frequently found in depths between two and ten metres. Records of A. compressiceps exist from all parts of Lake Tanganyika.

The features of the large, stretchable mouth armed with strong teeth suggest a predatory fish. Examinations of stomach contents and observations in the natural habitat as well as in captivity however, showed that this Cichlid does not prey upon other fishes. Although a fish is swallowed every now and then, these must have a surprisingly small size. The most important source of food in Lake Tanganyika is probably a small freshwater shrimp which this Cichlid is able to pick out of narrow rock crevices and similar places due to its pointed and laterally compressed body-shape.

Care

Keeping *Altolamprologus compressiceps* requires only comparatively small aquaria with a length of between a half to one metre if the fish are kept in pairs. It is a problem to obtain a harmonizing pair as the degree of intraspecific aggression is fairly high. It is therefore recommendable to keep several specimens together in a tank of approximately one and a half metres in length until a firm bonding between two specimens can be observed. The aquarium should be decorated in such a manner that rock constructions offer a variety of caves which also enable the specimens to define the borders

of their territories. As is the case in the other representatives of the genus, A. compressiceps is very tolerant towards plants and does not even damage delicate shoots.

A. compressiceps is a very timid fish which rarely swims around a lot and offers little resistance towards other fishes. It is therefore not advisable to keep it together with more energetic and very active species such as representatives of the genera *Tropheus* or *Petrochromis*. Suitable company are the smaller species of *Julidochromis* and *Neolamprologus*.

Newly imported specimens may initially refuse flake-food, but *Daphnia* are usually readily taken. Adult fish require — especially if they are supposed to produce spawn — a potent diet which should include White Mosquito-larvae, and grated shrimp-meat.

The

breeding

necessitates that a pair of this fish is kept separately in a natural decorated aquarium. It is a cave brooder which cares for the eggs, larvae, and fry in a parental family-structure. To date, only a few attempts to breed this species in captivity were successful. The juveniles are very small and initially need to be fed with the nauplii of *Artemia salina*, the Brine Shrimp, and powdered flake-food. They grow relatively slowly and may have reached a length of only five centimetres after one year.

Helping hands to catch aquarium fishes are easily found on Lake Tanganyika

The Genus Aulonocara

REGAN, 1921

This endemic genus of Lake Malawi holds approximately twenty species of which however several have not yet been scientifically described. The group has become extremely popular amongst aquarists since it contains a couple of exceptionally attractive species with a size that makes them suitable for the aquarium in the living-room. The species of *Aulonocara* are also commonly referred to as "Peacock Cichlids".

Although the last revision of this genus was published as recently as in 1987, neither the taxonomy nor the systematics of the Peacock Cichlids nor the cladistic relationships within this group are finally clarified (STAECK 1988). The most important feature of the *Aulonocara*-species easily recognizable also for the layman is a number of pit-like depressions which are especially prominent in the lower head-region of the fish. They probably function as receptors that assist the fish to find its preferred food of microorganisms living in the sandy ground.

▶ Aulonocara baenschi

MEYER & RIEHL, 1985

This splendid fish with its several differently coloured populations has been known to aquarists as "Blue-headed Peacock" or "Yellow Peacock" since the late seventies. After a decade of not having a scientific name, a valid description was eventually published in 1985.

Males grow to a maximum length of just under twelve centimetres with the females being considerably smaller. The sexes of adult specimens are easily distinguished by clearly different colour-patterns. Males mainly have a golden to chrome-yellow colouration of the body and the fins. The lower part of the head shows tones of metallic azure-blue whereas the caudal fin has a pattern of horizontal golden yellow stripes on a light blue ground colouration.

In contrast to the outstanding colour-pattern of the males, the females are very inconspicuous. On an olive-grey to beige-grey ground-colour, they have a pattern of ten to eleven dark transversal bands between the operculum and the base of the tail. They

Male of *Aulonocara baenschi*

can hardly be distinguished from females of other species of *Aulonocara*. One should therefore be careful when it comes to socializing them with related species. Juveniles are coloured like the females and semi-adult males sometimes keep their juvenile pattern for a surprisingly long time, especially when a larger mature male with typical male-colours is present. On account of this, it occasionally happens that a specimen thought to be a female one day turns out to be in fact a male.

The

natural habitat

of this fish is restricted to three largely isolated areas in the southwestern part of Lake Malawi, i.e. the Maleri Islands, the Chidunga Rocks near the village of Chipoka, and the type locality Nkhomo Reef in the vicinity of Benga village. There, this Cichlid is found in the transitory zone between sandy and rocky ground. The males stick to a certain site and mostly reside in front of or in a rock crevice or cave which forms the centre of their territories. The fish has a relatively small mouth and probably feeds on insect larvae which they find in the sandy ground.

The three populations differ to a certain extent regarding the content of blue in the colouration of the head.

Care

Carning for this beautiful Peacock Cichlid is not difficult. The species requires an aquarium of at least one metre in length. The hind third of it should contain numerous caves and alcoves. It is advisable that rock constructions reach up to just below the water surface so that the specimens can also use the upper half of the tank. Since these Cichlids are tolerant towards plants, it is possible to decorate the aquarium with the latter. In order to not further limit the swimming space, which has already been reduced by the rock constructions, one

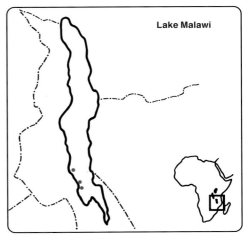

Localities of *Aulonocara baenschi*

should forgo tall-growing plants and give preference to those which remain low. By using the West African species of *Anubias* and the Java-fern *Microsorum pteropus* which anchor themselves to stones, even the constructions on the rear tank-wall can be greened. The decoration should be arranged in such a manner that its structure enables the fish to define the borders between their territories. The water should be of moderately hard quality and be neutral to alkaline.

The "Yellow Peacock" cannot be kept in pairs since the males frequently chase the females. Instead, a male should have two or three female specimens available. It is also not advisable to keep this species on its own in an aquarium. Positive experiences were made with this fish when it was kept together with other Malawi Cichlids. As the "Yellow Peacock" offers little resistance towards other fishes, it is impossible to keep it with strong and aggressive Cichlids. One should therefore forgo the large Haplochromines as well as most of the Mbuna-species and especially those of the genus *Melanochromis*. Adequate alternatives are found amongst the moderately large Cichlids of the Utaka-group which show a similar behaviour.

Males of the "Yellow Peacock" which feel uneasy because other, more aggressive fishes oppress them, loose their splendid yellow colouration, and become dirty yellowish brown. Two male specimens can only be kept in an extraordinarily large aquarium.

The

breeding

of this species is most promising in the community aquarium as described above. As the species belongs to the specialized mouth-brooders which form a mother-family structure, the males are always sexually active. More so, as soon as a female becomes ready to spawn, courtship activities increase considerably. With the body trembling and subsequent guiding, the male tries to attract the female to the spawning substrate. A preferred site for spawning is a horizontal stone-plate which lies inside a cave or which is at least covered from above.

The development from the fertilized egg to the juvenile able to swim takes nearly three weeks at temperatures around 26 °C. During this time, the female requires a sanctuary where it is left in peace by other fishes. If such place exists in the community tank, the female may remain there. Catching the specimen in an attempt to transfer it to another aquarium always carries the risk that eggs or larvae are spat out. If one wants to rear the entire fry, one should wait until the larval development is nearly completed and only then catch the female. After being transferred to a separate tank where it is undisturbed, it will soon release the juveniles from the mouth.

The parental care of the female then lasts at least one week. The juveniles already measure approximately ten millimetres and immediately feed on *Cyclops* and ground flake-food.

Swampy zone of shallow water on the northwestern shore of Lake Malawi (Itungi Port)

▶ *Aulonocara hueseri*
MEYER, RIEHL & ZETZSCHE, 1987

This "Peacock Cichlid" has also been imported alive for the first time in the late seventies and is therefore well known to aquarists. Due to the fact that another decade passed until its formal description was published, there was no scientific name available and consequently a variety of common names had been created in the meantime. Names such as "Yellow-bellied Peacock", *Aulonocara* "Night", and *Aulonocara* "White Top" all refer to this fish.

Males of this species reach a maximum size of approximately twelve centimetres whereas females grow up to eleven. Due to a clear sexual dichromatism adult males and females are easily distinguished. Head and nape of mature male specimens have a bright metallic gentian to ultramarine-blue colouration whilst the belly-region is chromeyellow. On a light blue ground, the caudal fin

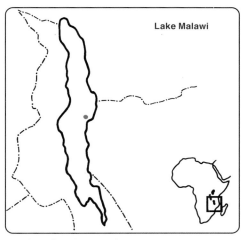

Locality of *Aulonocara hueseri*

carries a pattern of horizontal golden yellow stripes. The anal fin shows a number of larger, oval, pastel-orange spots. Females and juveniles are inconspicuously olive grey

Male of the Yellow-chested Peacock, *Aulonocara hueseri*

to beige grey and have approximately eleven dark transversal stripes.

The

natural distribution

of these Cichlids appear to be restricted to a very small area. The only known locality to date lies on the eastern shore of Likoma Island. Here, the fish occurs in larger numbers at a depth of twenty metres in the transitory zone from sandy to rocky ground. Its habitat is characterized by sandy interspaces of up to one square metre between numerous large rocks and boulders which form many crevices and caves. The males are obviously territorial and defend an area with a hiding-place in its centre.

Catching this fish is a problem. Since its biotope is fairly deep, collectors depend on scuba equipment. Furthermore, the specimens cannot be brought to the surface immediately after they have been caught. In order to prevent them from dying or being seriously harmed by the different pressures, they need to be kept at a lower depth for several hours before they can be transported further.

Care

This Peacock Cichlid is generally easily kept since this species requires moderately hard water with slightly alkaline to neutral features. The aquarium should at least be one metre in length. According to the conditions in the natural biotope of this Cichlid, the decoration should consist of rock constructions which provide numerous caves and other sanctuaries and simultaneously enable the specimens to define various territories.

As is the case with other specialized mouthbrooders, this species cannot be kept in pairs since the permanently courting male would cause constant stress to the female. Best results in the keeping and breeding of this fish were gained when it was kept together with other Malawi-Cichlids in a community-aquarium and the male could divide his attention between two or three females.

This Cichlid also shows little resistance towards other species. It is therefore inadequate for socialization with more aggressive or distinctly larger fishes. Positive results were obtained from experiments where it was kept together in the same aquarium with small and moderately large species of *Protomelas* and *Copadichromis* of the Utaka-group.

In contrast to the natural habitat where there are no higher plants, the aquarium can be greened without problems. The fish is tolerant towards plants and does not dig in a tank which corresponds with its natural requirements.

If the above mentioned hints for its husbandry are adhered to, the

breeding

of this Cichlid is no problem. A flat stone which lies in a rock crevice is a preferred spawning-site. As is the case in other specialized mouthbrooders, the offspring is reared in mother-family. In a natural aquarium with no over-population there is no necessity to remove the mother-specimen.

On the other hand, very few young fish will eventually reach adulthood. If one intends to rear the complete fry, one should transfer the female to a separate small tank shortly before the larval development is completed. At temperatures around 26 °C it takes approximately three weeks from spawning to this point of time. Given the opportunity to finalize its parental care the rearing of the juveniles is easy. When released from the mouth of the mother, they already measure approximately one centimetre and are capable of feeding on small Daphnia or crushed flake-food such as TetraMin or TetraCichlid.

◗ *Aulonocara stuartgranti*
MEYER & RIEHL, 1985

This blue Peacock Cichlid has become known amongst aquarists under the trade-name *Aulonocara* "Chilumba". Specific col-our-traits of this species are primarily the regular pattern of nine relatively narrow dark transversal stripes on the flanks between the edge of the gill-cover and the base of the tail, as well as the absence of a black submarginal band in the dorsal and anal fins.

The type locality of *Aulonocara stuart-granti* lies on the northwestern shore of Lake Malawi in the vicinity of the village of Chilumba. A Peacock Cichlid with a highly resembling colouration which has become known under the trade-name *Aulonocara* "Blue Regal" occurs in the shore zone of Mbenji Island several hundred kilometres afar to the south of the lake. Despite the geographical separation of both populations

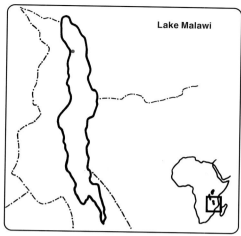

Locality of *Aulonocara stuartgranti*

and the obvious differences in their colour-ations, MEYER and co-authors (1985, 1987) consider this a population of *Aulonocara stuartgranti* — an opinion which is not with-out criticism.

Male of *Aulonocara stuartgranti*

◆ *Aulonocara* sp.
"Usisya"

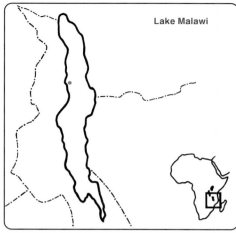

Locality of *Aulonocara* sp. "Usisya"

was exported for the first time in the early eighties. As far as is currently known, this Peacock Cichlid cannot undoubtedly be assigned to any of the known species. All such attempts — even if they were not marked as such — are hypothetic and lack evidence: MEYER et al. (1987) treated the "Usisya-Peacock" as *Aulonocara baenschi* MEYER & RIEHL, 1985; KONINGS (1989) considered it to be a population of *Aulonocara stuartgranti* MEYER & RIEHL, 1985; and SPREINAT (1989) did not allocate it to a certain species, but presumed that this fish might possibly belong to a population of *Aulonocara steveni* MEYER et al., 1987, as there is a high degree of resemblance regarding the colouration of both these Peacock Cichlids.

Besides a yellow body-colouration, the blueish black areas of the ventral, dorsal, and anal fins are the most important specific features of the "Usisya Peacock". Its range is extremely limited and confined to a reef off Mpandi Point in the neighbourhood of Usisya Village.

Male of *Aulonocara* sp. "Usisya"

The Genus Benthochromis

POLL, 1986

The genus *Benthochromis* which belongs to the tribe Limnochromini was described only recently by the Belgian ichthyologist POLL in 1986. It accommodates two species of Cichlids which, until then, were included in the genus *Haplotaxodon*. Specific traits of the *Benthochromis*-species are amongst others the slender elongate body-shape, the relatively large eyes, and a slightly protruding lower jaw. Presently, the genus only contains the two species *Benthochromis tricoti* and *Benthochromis melanoides* (POLL, 1984). As the generic name indicates, these fishes are inhabitants of great depths and live near the bottom.

◗ *Benthochromis tricoti*

(POLL, 1948)

The first imports of this interesting Cichlid reached Europe in 1989. Due to their eco-logy and their appearance one might assume they are extremely huge members of the genus *Paracyprichromis;* the body is slender and elongate, and the pointed head has a tube-like protrudable mouth. The spinous section of the dorsal fin is conspicuously low. Males have a caudal fin with filamentous appendices on the top and bottom edges and the ventral fins are also enlarged and pointed.

The ground-colouration of courting males is a dark greyish brown. The lateral sides of the body are marked with three narrow, bright light blue, longitudinal zigzag-lines. The lower part of the head is often bright yellow in colour whereas the upper gleams light blue. The anal fin is yellowish. The dark grey caudal fin has two narrow blue transversal stripes as well as top and bottom edges of the same colour. The ventral fins are blackish.

As this fish has a distinctly developed sexual dichromatism and fin dimorphism distinguishing between the sexes is easy. Female specimens, which are inconspicuously coloured greyish brown to silvery,

Male of *Benthochromis tricoti*

neither have any striped pattern in their fins nor on the body. They furthermore lack the filamentous prolongation of the fins which is typical for adult males. The maximum length of *Benthochromis tricoti* lies at 20 cm.

The
natural habitat

of *Benthochromis tricoti* is the lower rocky littoral. With some justification, the fish can be referred to as a "Deep-water Cichlid" — which is also taken into consideration for the generic name — as they exclusively live at the lower levels of Lake Tanganyika, i.e. at depths between 50 and 150 metres. The upper limit of their range is approximately 30 metres. Preferred habitats are vertical rockfaces on steep shores. Localities of *Benthochromis tricoti* have been recorded from the south of Lake Tanganyika (Zambia), from along the central western shore (Zaïre), the central eastern shore (Tanzania), and the northwest (Zaïre). The live specimens imported to date all originate from Zambia. Despite the considerable size, these fish feed on plankton and — as is the case with the Cichlids of the genera *Cyprichromis* and *Paracyprichromis* — mainly prey upon Copepods and other small shrimps. As an adaption to this type of prey they have a stretchable, far protrudable mouth which — as can be observed when *Cyclops* are fed — serves as a sucking tube.

Care

Keeping *Benthochromis tricoti* still lets the aquarist face certain problems. However, taking some general factors duly into consideration these can be solved. On account of their size, these fish require a spacious aquarium with a length of at least one and a half metres. Coarse sand has proven to be especially adequate. By means of some large stone-plates, the aquarium should be decorated in such a manner that the fish find

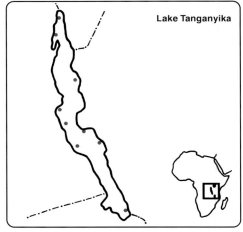

Localities of *Benthochromis tricoti*

cave-like hiding-places and have sufficient space for swimming. Although plants in this aquarium are unnatural, their usage is optional.

As in the case of other maternal mouthbrooders, this Cichlid should not be kept in pairs but in groups of one or two males with several females. This is the only way to prevent the females from suffering from the constant courtship activities and pursuits of the males.

Finally, special attention must be paid to a varying and quantitatively adequate diet. In general, it would certainly be impossible to keep a Cichlid of this size and appetite on a diet of Daphnia. It is therefore fortunate that this fish adjusts to all common types of food as long as the particles are relatively small.

Breeding

Courting males defend a more or less horizontal rockface as spawning site. *Benthochromis tricoti* belongs to the ovophile maternal mouthbrooders where the female alone cares for the offspring from spawning to completion of the larval development.

The description of the Genus

Chalinochromis

dates back recently. It was originally initiated when the Belgian ichthyologist POLL received a number of fish from the Burundian ornamental fish exporter BRICHARD with the request to assist with identification. Examination of the specimens revealed that it was an undescribed species which could not be assigned to any existing genus. Therefore, the original description of the species was published together with the diagnosis of the new Cichlid genus in 1974. Since then, two further representatives of the genus have been discovered on the central eastern shore of Lake Tanganyika in Tanzania which differ regarding their colourations, but which still await a formal description. In 1989, BRICHARD described another species with a bifurcate caudal fin as *Chalinochromis popelini*. Although no information is available on the precise collecting locality, it is believed to be on the western shore of the lake.

► *Chalinochromis brichardi*
POLL, 1974

reaches a maximum length of approximately twelve centimetres. A definite identification of the sex based on external features is impossible in this species. It is only in very old males that the dorsal and anal fins are generally more enlarged than in females. Sometimes there is also an indication of a fat-bulge on the nape.

A specific trait of all species of *Chalinochromis* are the black harness-stripes on the snout and the nape. In contrast to other representatives of the genus, *C. brichardi* lacks black markings on its flanks, the body is uniformly beige to light ivory coloured.

Chalinochromis brichardi has a relatively wide distribution in Lake Tanganyika, but does not necessarily occur where a respective biotope exists.

Chalinochromis brichardi

The

natural habitats

which have to date become known, all lie in the northeastern corner of Lake Tanganyika (Burundi), in northern Tanzania, and in the south (Zambia). It is certain that it does not occur on the central eastern shore. This fish is native to the rocky littoral. The preferred water-depth apparently lies between two and ten metres. They always reside in the proximity of crevices and other hiding-places.

Care

According to experiences *Chalinochromis brichardi* does not make great demands on the water chemistry. Keeping this Cichlid may also be successful in a relatively small aquarium if one has a harmonic pair. In such case, a tank of only 50 to 60 centimetres may be sufficient. Being an inhabitant of a rocky environment, the fish obviously require rock-constructions which offer an adequate number of hiding-sites to feel at ease. All *Chalinochromis* are timid fishes which patrol their territories relatively slowly with frequent breaks to observe the vicinity. As they are generally tolerant towards plants, the aquarium may be greened. It is however recommendable to choose hard-leaved plants, since some individuals occasionally chew on delicate shoots.

It is also advisable to keep this Cichlid in a large community aquarium. The fish can be socialized with all species which live in the rubble- or rocky littoral of Lake Tanganyika, i.e. especially with the numerous species of the genera *Tropheus, Neolamprologus, Julidochromis, Telmatochromis,* and *Petrochromis.*

Feeding newly imported specimens can sometimes be problematic as those specimens would not accept flake-food, but only live food. If they are added to adjusted specimens, the factor of food-jealousy usually has the result that the *Chalinochromis* also

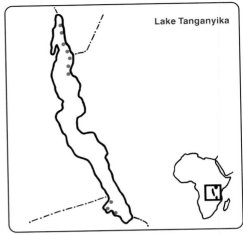

Localities of *Chalinochromis brichardi*

become accustomed to this unusual type of food.

Due to unknown reasons, the

breeding

has to date been successful in only relatively few instances. Most breedings were not successful with wild-caught specimens, but with captive-bred ones which were already accustomed to the conditions in the aquarium. All *Chalinochromis* are cave brooders which usually attach their spawn to the ceiling or a wall of their grotto or crevice. The partners display a close bonding to each other and care for the fry in a parental family.

Reproduction may be successful in a species tank as well as in an appropriately decorated community aquarium. Since the juveniles are very small, they must initially be fed with the nauplii of the Brine Shrimp or finely crushed TetraMin flake-food. In contrast to the West African cave brooders, the juveniles do not form a school which is guided by the parents, but they are individualists which show an affinity to the territory of the parents. Both the latter viciously defend it against any enemy.

The Genus Copadichromis

ECCLES & TREWAVAS, 1989

Both the mentioned authors recently established this genus to accommodate 17 species which are all endemic to Lake Malawi and which has previously been placed in the collective genus *Haplochromis*. All of them are small to moderately large fishes whose standard lengths range between eight and sixteen centimetres. Due to their largely identic ecology and requirements African fishermen refer to them as Utaka. All these Cichlids feed on plankton and often occur in very large shoals along the vertical cliffs of underwater reefs where the currents provide ample food. The Cichlids of the genera *Cyprichromis* and *Paracyprichromis* in Lake Tanganyika have a comparable ecology. In adaption to their prey, the Utaka-cichlids also have a very flexible and protrudable mouth which may function as a suckingtube for feeding.

Since the Utaka-cichlids occur in such large numbers on the underwater-reefs, they can obviously be caught in bulk without great effort. This is the reason why these fishes, despite their small size, represent an important source of food for the local people.

The pattern of dark markings is not a constant trait within the genus *Copadichromis*. Together with transversally banded species, there are others with longitudinal stripes or with up to three lateral blotches. This clearly indicates that the species presently assigned to the genus *Copadichromis* are not of monophyletic origin and the morphological and anatomical similarities are based upon a convergent evolution which is initiated by their highly specialized feeding ecology. It is therefore to be expected that not all of them will permanently remain in this cladistic unit. Added by three new descriptions in 1990, their total number has meanwhile increased to twenty.

Since the males of many *Copadichromis* species display strinkingly splendid colours,

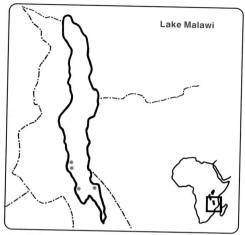

Localities of *Copadichromis azureus*

they belong to the most popular Cichlids for the hobby.

▶ *Copadichromis azureus*

KONINGS, 1990

Although this Cichlid has for years been known to aquarists, its scientific description as a new species only dates back recently. In older aquaristic books it is referred to as *Haplochromis chrysonotus* "Mbenji" and *H. chrysonotus* "Maleri".

Only reaching a maximum length of around twelve centimetres, *Copadichromis azureus* is one of the smaller Utaka-cichlids. The sexes are easily distinguished as the species has a well developed sexual dichromatism. Adult males present themselves in a bright metallic blue not only on the head and body, but also on the unpairy fins. The dorsal fin has a narrow light margin whereas the anal and ventral fins are mainly smoke-black in colour. Depending on the mood, up to ten narrow, dark, transversal lines may appear on the flanks between the edge of the gill-cover and the caudal peduncle. However, the most conspicuous feature of this species is the three black blotches on the lateral side of the body. The anterior two lie between the lateral lines. The first one is situated approximately between the eighth and twelfth scale, the second lies below the posteriormost rays of the dorsal fin, and the third is found on the posterior portion of the caudal peduncle. Whilst this spotted pattern is always visible in females and juveniles, it is often overlaid by the stripes described above or even completely suppressed in dominant courting male specimens.

In contrast to the very conspicuous males, the females appear in a very modest greyish brown colouration with the three lateral blotches being clearly set off.

The

natural habitat

of *Copadichromis azureus* lies in the southern part of Lake Malawi. Localities are known from the western shore (Nkhomo Reef, Mbenji Island, Maleri Islands) as well as from the southeastern shore (Eccles Reef near the village Makanjila). The species prefers the lower littoral below depths of

approximately ten metres. Courting males conglomerate in the transitory zone from rocky to sandy ground where they make their crater-like spawning-nests.

Care

Keeping *Copadichromis azureus* is not difficult. To suit this Cichlid, an aquarium of one and a half metres in length should be chosen. Sand and larger stones are required for its decoration which is assembled in such a way so as to separate the ground into sections. The keeping together with other small Haplochromines in a community tank has been proved successful.

Breeding

This fish belongs to the highly specialized mouthbrooders which do not engage in a firm partnership. The female alone cares for the fry which is released from the mouth approximately three weeks after spawning. The juveniles are already very independent by then.

Male of *Copadichromis azureus*

◗ *Copadichromis borleyi*
(ILES, 1960)

This Cichlid reaches a length of approximately thirteen centimetres. As males and females are differently coloured, distinguishing between them is easy.

An obvious feature of the males is the presence of extremely enlarged ventral fins which are white to light blueish on the anterior edges and which may reach the posterior margin of the anal fin in old specimens. The head and anterior part of the back are coloured in a metallic, gleaming, ultramarine blue whereas the rest of the body is honey-yellow.

Females look drab dusty grey. The silvery shining flanks are marked with three black blotches. The first is the largest and lies immediately below the lateral line between the ninth and twelfth scale. The second one is situated immediately above the lower lateral line and below the last rays of the dorsal fin, whilst the third blotch marks the centre of the caudal peduncle.

The

natural habitats

of this species are the rocky littorals of Lake Malawi. It seems that the fish has a fairly wide range and it is commonly found above underwater reefs.

The species belongs to the Utaka-cichlids which temporarily inhabit the regions of free water near the shores. It is a specialized predator upon zooplankton and sucks in its food by means of its specially protrudable mouth. Males, ready to breed, become territorial and claim an area in the rocky zone with a spawning site in its centre. It is usually the horizontal, smooth, upper side of a boulder.

Male of *Copadichromis borleyi*

For a

Care

which takes the most important requirements into consideration spacious aquaria are required which have a length of more than one meter. Besides the obligatory stones, plants may also be used for their decoration as these are not damaged by the fish. It must be ensured that adequate swimming space remains.

Best results were achieved when a male was kept together with several females and other Malawi-cichlids in a community aquarium. Since *C. borleyi* belongs to the relatively peaceful Cichlids, such an aquarium should be free of aggressive species.

As is the case with the majority of East African mouthbrooders,

breeding

in the community aquarium is preferred. A horizontal stone-plate is usually chosen as spawning-site. The courtship follows the commonly known pattern of African mouthbrooders and the juveniles are cared

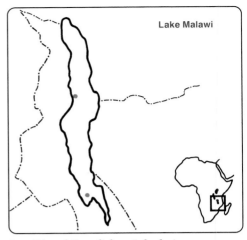

Localities of *Copadichromis borleyi*

for by the mother alone. At a water-temperature of 26 °C, the development of the eggs and larvae takes about three weeks. When the juveniles eventually leave the mouth of their mother, they are already fairly sized and independent. They may be fed with small Daphnia and powdered flake-food.

Rocky littoral in the southwest of Lake Malawi (Otter Point)

The description of the genus

Cyphotilapia

by REGAN dates back to 1920. Besides a species from Lake Tanganyika he originally included another one from the upper Congo which was later re-allocated to the genus *Thoracochromis*. Therefore, the genus is monotypical today, but two subspecies or colour morphs are known.

▶ Cyphotilapia frontosa
(BOULENGER, 1906)
Five-striped subspecies

The type specimen of this species was collected by CUNNINGTON in the vicinity of Kigoma and belongs to the northeastern subspecies which, as can also be depicted from BOULENGER's drawing, differs from the other and much more frequently kept subspecies portrayed here, as it has six instead of five dark transversal bands between the edge of the gill-cover and the caudal fin.

It is amazing that POLL, who was the first to describe the form with five transversal bands and also illustrate it in a drawing and several photographs in 1956, obviously did not realize that the specimen described and figured by BOULENGER had an additional transversal band.

Cyphotilapia frontosa reaches more than thirty centimetres in length and may weigh half a kilogram. The most prominent feature of this species is a shapeless fat-bulge on the forehead which is especially prominent in old males. Another feature enabling one to distinguish between the sexes is the size and shape of the fins. Adult male specimens have distinctly enlarged ventral, anal, and dorsal fins with filamentous appendices.

The

natural distribution

of the five-striped subspecies is distinctly larger than that of the six-striped one. Confirmed records have been made in the northern (Burundi) as well as in the southern

Cyphotilapia frontosa, subspecies with five transversal bands

41

(Zambia) corner of the lake. In between, the fish was also found on the western shore which belongs to Zaïre. The fish exclusively lives in the rocky zone with adult specimens only inhabiting the lower regions of the shore at depths between 30 and 40 metres. Here, they occur in larger conglomerations. On the other hand they are rarely found above twenty metres, and it is usually individual juveniles which reside at the upper levels. Since specimens caught at greater depths have to be adjusted to lower pressure carefully and slowly, catching this species is difficult and irksome.

Despite their large size, this Cichlid is not necessarily a predatory fish in nature. As was found during examinations of stomach-contents, it preferably feeds on freshwater shrimps. Small fishes are seldom preyed upon.

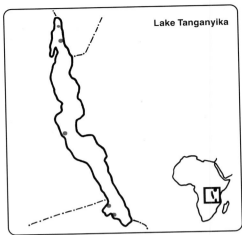

Localities of the Five-banded subspecies of *Cyphotilapia frontosa*

Care

Keeping adult specimens is only possible in very large aquaria exceeding one and a half metres in length. Although *Cyphotilapia* has a space-requirement which is small in relation to its size because it is timid and hardly swims around, it cannot be kept in pairs. Being a maternal mouthbrooder, a male should have several females around him.

Keeping this fish together with other, even smaller Tanganyika-cichlids is possible and would especially take the larger species of *Neolamprologus* into consideration. Representatives of the genera *Tropheus* and *Petrochromis* are less adequate company as they are too active and nervous for the *Cyphotilapia*.

Being an inhabitant of the rocky zone, these Cichlids require rockconstructions which provide them with hiding sites and enable them to define territories. Large Cichlids obviously require potent food to stay healthy. An optimal diet will therefore include shrimp-meat which one can obtain as frozen shrimps. In addition, ox-heart, earthworms, and TetraCichlid or TetraCichlid Sticks may be fed.

The courtship, which is the first sign of

breeding

activities, proceeds in a simple way and is inconspicuous. The fish is a mouthbrooder which rears its offspring in a mother-family. Due to the fact that the eggs are large and rich in yolk, their incubation-period is relatively long. At a water-temperature of 26 °C it takes approximately four weeks until the fairly independent juveniles leave the mouth of their mother for the first time. They are easy to rear with small *Daphnia* and powdered flake-food. In a natural species-aquarium with adequate hiding-places they will grow up even in the presence of adult conspecifics.

Cyphotilapia is not very productive, and even fully grown females will rarely have more than fifty eggs. Strict attention should be paid in all breeding attempts that the two subspecies are not hybridized. Cross-breed often have five bands on one side and six or the other.

Another genus which exclusively accommodates Tanganyika-cichlids is

Cyprichromis.

It presently contains three closely resembling species which had previously been assigned to the genus *Limnochromis*. Due to certain features, SCHEUERMANN transferred them to a separate new systematic unit in 1977.

◆ Cyprichromis microlepidotus
(POLL, 1956)

reaches a maximum body length of around ten centimetres. Since the fish has developed a distinct sexual dichromatism, the identification of the sexes does not cause problems. Female specimens are inconspicuous greenish brown to khaki-grey with the flanks having a silvery shine.

On the other hand, the males are particularly colourful. Being an exception amongst the Tanganyika-cichlids, they show a polychromatism, which means that even specimens from the same locality may look different. Whilst one morph may have a golden yellow caudal fin, it may be blackish blue or turquoise-blue in another. The upper half of the body is beige, and the flanks are marked with irregular light blue gleaming stripes. The tips of the ventral fins are golden yellow.

The

natural distribution

of this Cichlid appears to be fairly limited. All localities known to date lie in the northern half of the lake, i.e. in Burundi, Zaïre, and Tanzania. The fish are mainly observed in rocky zones of the shore where they reside in large shoals along steep faces. They

Male of *Cyprichromis microlepidotus;* morph with the yellow caudal fin

appear to be bound to a specific location to a surprising extent. They are usually only found at greater depths with the top border being approximately ten metres. Although the species is not common, it is always found in large groups. In their natural environment, they preferably prey upon small Copepodid shrimps which they scavenge with the assistance of the tube-like protrudable mouth.

Care

As far as carning for *Cyprichromis microlepidotus* is concerned, it is obvious that specimens must never be kept on their own, but always in groups. Single specimens or even a pair do not feel at ease and often suffer. If one decides on this species, one should require at least half a dozen specimens. Since *Cyprichromis* does not develop a bonding between the reproduction partners, such a group should contain more females than males.

It is also important to know that this fish requires a lot of space for swimming. Consequently, the aquarium should have a minimum length of at least one metre. As the fish completely ignores plants and also does not

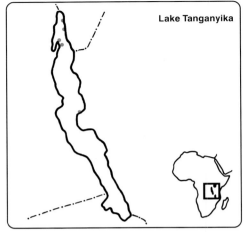

Localities of *Cyprichromis microlepidotus*

dig, it is ideal for a planted tank. The chosen plants should however not limit the swimming space. In the natural biotope of this species there are no plants except algae.

Due to the fact that all the *Cyprichromis* species offer little resistance towards other fish, they are inadequate for a community aquarium which also houses more aggressive Cichlids. Species with a more ground-dwelling habit, such as the smaller species

Cyprichromis are found in the lower rocky littoral. Two fighting males of *C. leptosoma* at a depth of five metres.

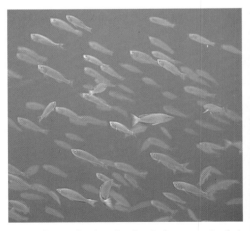

Cyprichromis live in schools: *C. leptosoma* in their natural habitat.

of *Julidochromis* or the Goby Cichlids appear to be ideal because the *Cyprichromis* prefer the free space in the top half of the tank.

All *Cyprichromis* are adapted to small-sized prey. The ideal food is therefore Daphnia and *Cyclops* as well as flake-food like TetraMin or TetraCichlid. Newly imported specimens will however initially accept only live food and have to get used to other food. The adjustment period can take up to half a year, but is drastically shortened if the aquarium already houses specimens accustomed to flake-food.

The

breeding

of this interesting Cichlid has been successful in only a few exceptional instances. The major reason for this however is that the species is very seldom imported. Amongst the Cichlids, *Cyprichromis* is singled out in so far that the eggs are laid in the free water and not on a substrate of whatever kind.

Under captive conditions, the vivid courtship and the spawning act take place near the water surface. Once an egg has been ejected, the female turns around in a flash, follows the sinking egg, and takes it into the mouth. As is the case in other specialized mouthbrooders, the eggs are only fertilized in the mouth of the mother specimen by swimming through the visible cloud of sperm.

At a water-temperature of 26 °C, it takes approximately three weeks until the mother releases the fry from her mouth. Since the skin of the female's throat is thin and translucent, the development of the juveniles can be observed from outside. They are not taken back into the mouth of the mother. The juveniles are already fairly independent at this stage and form a school residing immediately below the water surface. They feed on selected small *Cyclops* and *Daphnia*, but also accept finely crushed TetraMin or TetraCichlid. Due to the fact that adult *Cyprichromis* do not prey upon their juveniles, it is obviously recommendable to breed them in a species aquarium.

Those Tanganyika-cichlids that are most interesting for the aquarium live in the rubble- and rocky littoral.

The Genus *Fossorochromis*

ECCLES & TREWAVAS, 1989

is endemic to Lake Malawi and the Shire River. It accommodates only one species which is frequently kept in aquaria despite its large size. Its separate systematic status is mainly based upon its conspicuous colour-pattern which is unique amongst the Cichlids of Lake Malawi.

▶ *Fossorochromis rostratus*

(BOULENGER, 1899)

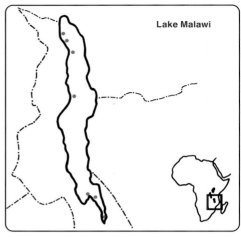

Localities of *Fossorochromis rostratus*

may reach a size exceeding twenty centimetres. The sexual dichromatism of this species is so extreme that a layman would hardly ever recognize that the males and females belong to the same species. The lateral sides of the female's body are marked with a longitudinal row of five large, black blotches at the level of the eye. In addition there is a second row of usually only four blotches immediately below the base of the dorsal

fin. Several more spots may occasionally be present on the fin-base. The background-colouration of these specimens is greenish beige.

Fully coloured males lack any spotted pattern. They are uniformly yellowish grey with a pretty gleam of copper-red on the

Male of *Fossorochromis rostratus*

46

head and body. The dorsal, anal, and caudal fins are mainly azure-blue. Courting specimens have the ventral fins and the lower portion of the body coloured pitch black whilst the nape shines silvery green.

The

natural habitats

of this species lie in the shore-zone of Lake Malawi and in the Shire River and consist of sandy areas. Semi-adult specimens often form large schools which I could also observe in the rocky littoral. Above sandy ground, this Cichlid shows a peculiar escape behaviour. In a case of acute danger, the fish rapidly bury themselves in the ground. I could observe them doing so on a couple of occasions when diving and trying to manoeuvre them into a net.

The species is widely distributed in its home waters and ranks amongst the commonest Cichlids. They find their food mainly whilst digging in the sand. Adult specimens most likely also prey upon fishes.

Care

The perfect conditions for keeping this large Cichlid require an aquarium of one and a half metres at minimum. The species should not be kept on its own, but in company of other Malawi-cichlids. Through this, their intraspecific aggression is reduced to a bearable measure. This fish is tolerant towards other Cichlids. Adequate company-fishes are preferably found amongst the Haplochromines and the Mbuna-cichlids of the genera *Melanochromis* or *Pseudotropheus*.

The decoration of the aquarium should primarily consist of large rocks which are used to structure the ground and to provide hiding sites. Since *F. rostratus* is relatively tolerant towards plants, these may also be used for decoration. However, one should give hardy and fast-growing species preference. Being able to adjust to all types of food, the diet is no problem. Larger specimens would obviously require adequate

quantities, especially if the females are to develop spawn. In this case, fish, shrimps, and earthworms should be taken into consideration.

In this species, it has also turned out that a

breeding

attempt is most promising in a community-aquarium. Being a specialized mouth-breeder, the female *Fossochromis rostratus* alone cares for and rears the fry. A clutch of a moderately sized fish contains between fifty and one hundred eggs. Spawning usually takes place on the horizontal surface of a smooth stone.

In order to prevent a large number of the juveniles being preyed upon by other fishes in the aquarium, the mother specimen should be transferred to a separate tank after approximately two weeks. There, she can care for the young ones undisturbed. The diet of the juveniles consists of selected small *Daphnia* and crushed flake-food, e.g. TetraCichlid. Provided with sufficient quantities of food and regular exchanges of the water, they grow surprisingly quickly.

Transitory zone from the rocky to the sandy zone. Littoral of Likoma Island at four metres depth.

The Genus Gnathochromis

POLL, 1981

is also one of the more recently described genera. It was established by POLL to accommodate two species of Cichlids which are endemic to Lake Tanganyika and which until then were assigned to the genus *Limnochromis*. The most important shared feature of the species of *Gnathochromis* is the low-set mouth which can be widely protruded and which works like a sucking-tube during feeding. At present, *Gnathochromis permaxillaris* and *G. pfefferi* are the only two representatives of this genus.

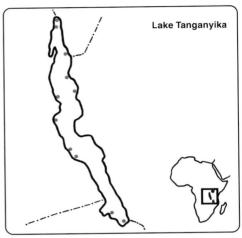

Localities of *Gnathochromis permaxillaris*

▶ Gnathochromis permaxillaris

(DAVID, 1936)

This highly interesting Cichlid was offered in fair numbers by the pet-shop industry for the first time in 1990. The late export date is explained by the fact that this fish lives in such great depths that the catching of these

fish for the aquarium requires considerable effort.

Gnathochromis permaxillaris can reach a length of well above fifteen centimetres. The fish is fairly high-backed with the body greatly compressed laterally. The most distinct identification trait is the very short lower jaw which is considerably exceeded

Gnathochromis permaxillaris

by the thick projected upper lip. The ground-colouration is more yellowish in specimens from northern collecting sites and usually brown in those from the south of the lake. The flanks of the body are marked with a number of glossy, light blue scales which may be regarded as four or five fairly irregular longitudinal rows. The dorsal, anal, and caudal fins are dark grey to slightly blueish and often have a multitude of small yellowish speckles. In both sexes, the ventral fins are extremely enlarged and end in filamentous appendices. Despite statements to the contrary — which are all based upon POLL (1956) — the females do not have longer fins. As there are no distinctly developed differences between males and females, the sex can only be determined to a certain degree by the size of the urogenital papilla which is smaller in male specimens.

The
natural habitat

of *Gnathochromis permaxillaris* is the deeper levels of Lake Tanganyika. With some justification, these fish can be referred to as "Deep-water Cichlids" since they have been recorded from depths between fifty and one hundred metres of depth, but may also occur below that. Localities are known from practically all parts of the lake.

Although the fish has occasionally been caught above rocky ground, records have been made much more frequently above muddy or sandy grounds (POLL 1956). It therefore seems as if it prefers soft substrates. The unusual shape of the mouth and examinations of stomach-contents indicate that this Cichlid exclusively preys upon micro-shrimps of the *Cyclops*-group and therefore is a specialized plankton feeder. As was observed under aquarium conditions, the fish primarily feed by searching the ground with the assistance of the widely protrudable mouth in a manner comparable with a vacuum cleaner.

Care

Keeping this fish should not cause specific problems if a variety of basic aspects is given attention to in order to make it feel at home.

Due to the adult size of the species, its husbandry requires spacious tanks which distinctly exceed one metre in length. The ground should not consist of gravel, but of coarse sand. Furthermore, a couple of large stone-plates are needed which one groups to form several caves as hiding-places for the fish. It should also be borne in mind that *Gnathochromis permaxillaris* is a very timid species with little resistance. Very vivid or even aggressive species are therefore absolutely inappropriate company fishes.

Although this Cichlid is a plankton feeder in its natural biotope, it willingly takes all types of food in the aquarium.

The
breeding

of *Gnathochromis permaxillaris* has already been successful on a couple of occasions. The fish is fairly productive with clutches containing between one and two hundred eggs. This Cichlid is a member of the small group of ovophile mouthbrooders in Lake Tanganyika with a biparental mouthbrooding pattern. Although the eggs are initially carried by the female, they are temporarily passed on to the male already on the second or third day which means that both parental specimens incubate the eggs and larvae by alternatingly carrying them in the mouth and passing them on to one another. Depending on the water-temperature, the juveniles can be observed swimming freely after approximately two weeks. The parental care is continued thereafter not only by chasing potential predators away from the fry, but by also taking them back into the mouth. The juveniles can easily be reared by feeding them newly hatched nauplii of the Brine Shrimp. They may already be two centimetres in length after four weeks.

The Genus Haplochromis

HILGENDORF, 1888

As a result of several step-by-step revisions by a variety of authors (GREENWOOD 1956, 1957, 1959, 1960, 1962, 1967, 1979, 1980, GREENWOOD & GEE 1968, ECCLES & TREWAVAS 1989) the original very large and heterogenous genus *Haplochromis* was drastically reduced to a mere half a dozen of species. Many Cichlids from Lake Tanganyika and Lake Malawi were re-allocated to a multitude of primarily new genera. However, this arrangement has recently been revised for the close to 200 species of Cichlids described to date from Lake Victoria and they are no longer kept in the twenty new genera described by GREENWOOD. The re-assignment of this group of species to *Haplochromis* is based upon new research (e.g. MEYER et al. 1990) which indicates that these Cichlids are of monophyletic origin, meaning all originate from the same ancestral form.

Ichthyologists presume that up to the second half of the seventies more than 300 different species of Cichlids lived in Lake Victoria (GOLDSCHMIDT & WITTE 1992). Although the members of this species group differ comparatively little with regard to their anatomies and morphologies, there are major deviations regarding their individual habitat requirements and especially the feeding ecologies. Specialized zooplankton and phytoplankton feeders were discovered amongst the species of *Haplochromis* of Lake Victoria, and others feed on detritus, algae, plants, insects, molluscs, or shrimps. Amongst those which prey upon fishes, not only scale-eaters were found, but also those which have specialized on stealing eggs or larvae from other mouthbrooders. Eventually, there are even cleaners in Lake Victoria which feed on the ectoparasites living on other fishes.

During the first half of the eighties it was abruptly disclosed that the variety of species of *Haplochromis,* and the number of individuals too, was dramatically diminishing in

The shoreline of Lake Victoria is often bordered by Papyrus-forests.

Lake Victoria. In some regions of the lake this was found to be based on overfishing. The major cause for the drastic reduction of the fish-population was however found to be the Nileperch *Lates niloticus* which had been introduced to Lake Victoria in the early eighties. Its population had suddenly exploded in many regions of the lake, and being a piscivorous fish, it had greatly reduced the *Haplochromis* species. More recently conducted research showed that approximately two thirds of the original more than three hundred species of *Haplochromis* had already become extinct in Lake Victoria or were at least subjected to severe threat (GOLDSCHMIDT & WITTE 1992).

Selected catching of certain fishes for the aquarium by divers is an important means of exporting ornamental fishes from Lakes Malawi and Tanganyika, but is impossible to conduct in Lake Victoria due to many reasons. Firstly, the water of the lake is usually so murky that a diver can see only a metre ahead. Secondly, diving in many parts of this lake holds the danger of infection with Bilharzia. Therefore, the fishes for the aquarium are caught in the same manner as those for the cooking pot, i.e. by large drag-nets. The results for the aquarium-fish exporter are therefore much more incidental than in the cases of the other two East African lakes.

Most of the *Haplochromis* species of Lake Victoria are ideal fishes for the aquarium owing to a number of reasons. Their pros include amongst others their comparatively small size as the majority of them are fully grown at ten centimetres. In addition to this, the males of many species are very colourful and therefore highly attractive. Furthermore, these Cichlids belong, as all others do which were placed into the generic group of the Haplochromines by ECCLES & TREWAVAS (1989), to the maternal mouthbrooders which do well under the special conditions of an aquarium and are easy to keep and breed. Despite the aforesaid, the species of *Haplochromis* from Lake Victoria have only played a fairly minor role

in the aquaristic hobby although first exports were already observed in the first half of the seventies. Out of the enormous diversity of forms, very few species have reached the aquaria of the enthusiasts. The majority of even these have only been kept occasionally and temporarily.

Table 6
Important data from Lake Victoria

Lake Victoria	
Clarity:	1 to 8 m
pH-value:	7,1—9,0
Conductivity at 20 °C:	90—145 micro-Siemens/cm
Average surface temp.:	24 °C

One of the reasons certainly is the fact that imports of these fishes were few and far between. A more important factor is that it is generally extremely difficult to identify the females of a certain species in order to assemble pairs. Whilst the males of most the species have typical and unmistakable courtship-colourations by which they can be distinguished without doubt, the females are inconspicuously silvery white or grey and all look more or less the same. Since there are furthermore many species which have closely resembling body-shapes, the specific identity of the females is difficult to securely determine in live specimens.

Another typical peculiarity also negatively affects the popularity of the species of *Haplochromis*. Although the males of many forms have fairly spectacular colour-patterns, these are only displayed to the full extent during courtship. Exposed to stress, e.g. shortly after being caught or in the undecorated overcrowded tank of a pet-shop, the colours quickly fade and the fish soon appear more or less as drab as the females.

▶ *Haplochromis nigricans*
(BOULENGER, 1906)

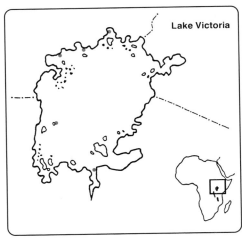

Localities of *Haplochromis nigricans*

On occasion of his revision of the Cichlids of Lake Victoria, GREENWOOD (1979, 1980) transferred this species to the genus *Neochromis* which REGAN had already suggested in 1920. Under aquarium conditions, the males reach a length of approximately twelve centimetres whilst females hardly exceed the ten centimetre mark. Courting males have a metallic shining greyish blue to dark blue body-colouration and a pattern of eight broad, pitch black, transversal bands whose intensity very much depends on the prevailing mood and is thus highly variable. The caudal fin is blackish at its base, but otherwise deep red. The mainly greyish blue anal fin also has a reddish tinge. The ventral fins are black. The dorsal fin is partly blueish, partly blackish and has a distinct bright red margin. Female specimens are inconspicuously greyish green to greyish brown. Besides this common form, an apparently very rare chequered morph has been described (GREENWOOD 1956) which has a pattern of black blotches on a yellow ground-colouration.

The
natural habitat
of *Haplochromis nigricans* lies in the upper region of the shore-zone. Being a vegetarian and feeding on the lawn of algae overgrow-

Male of *Haplochromis nigricans*

ing the surfaces, its distribution is restricted to areas with a rocky or stony ground. Examinations of stomach-contents (GREEN-WOOD 1956) indicated that infusorias, Green, and Blue Algae had been fed on. Although locality records of this species have mainly been made in the northern half of Lake Victoria, it has also been found in the southeast and thus appears to have a wider range than originally presumed.

Care

Keeping this hardy and adaptable fish is easy. Males specimens however claim large territories and therefore aquaria with a length of more than one metre are required. On the other hand, several males can be kept together in a spacious tank. *Haplochromis nigricans* should never be kept in pairs,
but one male should always be surrounded by a number of females. Its husbandry in a spacious community aquarium with other Cichlids from Lake Victoria is highly recommendable.

The tank should be decorated in such a manner that rock constructions and dense thickets of plants provide a sufficient number of hidingplaces and simultaneously simplify the division of the floor-space into several territories. The bottom should not be covered with gravel, but with coarse sand. The feeding of this fish also does not cause problems. Being almost an omnivore in captivity, all common types of food are accepted.

Breeding

Haplochromis nigricans is an ovophile, maternal mouthbrooder with no bonding between the partners. The male creates a small pit in his territory in which mating takes place. The mouthbrooding by the female lasts for almost two weeks depending on the water-temperature. Even after the juveniles have left the mouth, the care is continued for some time. Nauplii of the Brine Shrimp have been proven an adequate initial food.

Transitory zone from the sandy to the rocky littoral in Lake Victoria near Mwanza

◆ *Haplochromis nyererei*
WITTE-MAAS & WITTE, 1985

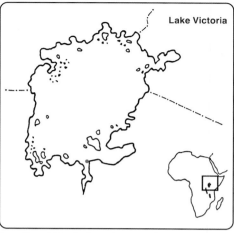

Lake Victoria

Locality of *Haplochromis nyererei*

Males of this splendidly coloured Cichlid from Lake Victoria reach a length of around ten centimetres under aquarium conditions whilst female are slightly smaller.

The colour features of courting males include a deep red zone which extends over forehead, nape, and back, and a blueish black to black area which ranges from the mouth over the throat, chest, and belly up to the caudal peduncle. The central parts of the flanks are marked with a yellowish green zone and several dark transversal bands. The ventral fins are black, and the distant portion of the caudal fin is red. The base of the dorsal fin is red whilst the rest is light blue. The anal fin is mainly light blue, reddish in its outer sections, and is patterned with two to four egg-shaped spots.

In contrast to the bright coloured males, the females are fairly dull greyish brown to light brown with a metallic gleam.

The locality records made so far all come from the southeastern part of Lake Victoria.

Here, the species was found at depths between 0,5 to 3,5 metres above rocky ground in the Gulf of Mwanza. The major source of food for this fish is zooplankton, but examinations of stomach-contents (WITTE-MAAS & WITTE 1985) showed that algae, insects, and especially mosquito-larvae were also preyed upon.

Male of *Haplochromis nyererei*

◗ *Haplochromis* sp.

This brightly coloured Cichlid from Lake Victoria was first imported in the second half of the seventies. Although it was assigned to a variety of species in the meantime, more recent studies indicate that it is in fact a separate taxon.

Male specimens can grow close to twelve centimetres whilst females are fully grown at approximately ten. Since this Cichlid has a clear sexual dichromatism, the identification of adult males and females is easy. The flanks of courting males appear in a grand cadmiumyellow with the head and nape being reddish orange. The throat and the belly region have a light blue background-colouration. Whilst the ventral fins are pitch black, all other fins have blue and red sections. On the other hand, females have a pattern of eight to nine dark transversal bands on a yellowish grey to silvery ground.

The presently known distribution of this Cichlid centres in the southeastern part of

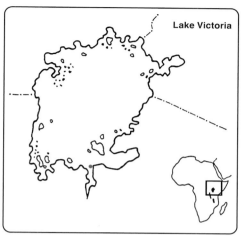

Localitiy of *Haplochromis* sp.

Lake Victoria with all exported specimens originating from the Gulf of Mwanza. Its preferred habitat is the rocky grounds of the shallow shore-zone.

Male of *Haplochromis* sp.

55

The Genus Hemitilapia
BOULENGER, 1902

The distribution of this monotypic genus is restricted to Lake Malawi. The justification for the systematically isolated position of its sole species is the special arrangement of the teeth and the very obvious pattern of large black blotches in the upper half of the body. Since the same pattern is also present in the three species of the genus *Trematocranus*, it may be presumed that these two genera are more closely related to one another.

◗ *Hemitilapia oxyrhynchus*
BOULENGER, 1902

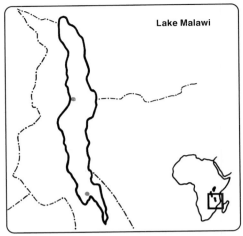

Localities of *Hemitilapia oxyrhynchus*

may reach a maximum length of close to twenty centimetres. Courting males can be recognized by their splendid colour-pattern. The entire body is turquoise-blue with the head region being very bright. The membranes of the caudal fin are marked with orange coloured dashes and dots, and the posterior portion of the dorsal fin also has a pattern of oval orange spots. Female specimens are silvery to yellowish grey. They have three large blotches on the back whose presence depends on the prevailing

Male of *Hemitilapia oxyrhynchus*

mood. One of these markings lies below the spinous portion of the dorsal fin, another one below the soft section, and the third one is found on the upper half of the base of the caudal peduncle.

The
natural habitat
of this species is the sandy littoral, and especially those areas which are vegetated with *Vallisneria*. In the meadows formed by these plants, the fish shows a peculiar feeding behaviour which has led to its name "*Vallisneria*-sucker". They feed on algae and microorganisms which have settled on the leaves of the *Vallisneria*-plants. In order to exploit this source of food, the fish lie on its side and take one of the long tape-like leaves with the pointed mouth in order to scratch off the food without damaging the plant.

Care

The successful keeping of *Hemitilapia oxyrhynchus* definitely requires a large aquarium of at least one and a half metres in length. The fish should not be kept in pairs if possible as the female is often constantly pursued by the male. The husbandry in a community aquarium is recommendable. Adequate company fishes can be chosen from the genera *Protomelas* and *Copadichromis* especially and one or two Mbuna-cichlids may be added.

Although this Cichlid is an inhabitant of the sandy zone, the decoration of the aquarium should not lack stone-plates which create hiding sites and divide the ground into several separated areas. With regard to the adult size this fish may grow to, the vegetation should obviously consist of large hardy plants. If it is intended to decorate the tank as natural as possible, *Vallisneria* should be planted and sand be chosen as substrate. Feeding this species does not cause any problems as all common types of food are accepted.

The
breeding
resembles that of other Haplochromines from Lake Malawi and will be successful if the hints given in their accounts are followed. *Hemitilapia oxyrhynchus* is also a mouthbrooder. The species is agamous, which means that there is no bonding between the partners. Rearing and caring for the fry is exclusive to the female. At approximately 26 °C, the development of the larvae is completed after almost three weeks and the juveniles leave the mouth of the mother for the first time. They are then fed with selected small *Daphnia* and crushed flake-food.

Sandy zone near Cape Maclear with the islands of Thumbi and Dombwe in the background

The Genus

Julidochromis

was established by BOULENGER as early as in 1898. Despite the additions of species during the past decades, it has remained a very small systematic unit. To date, only five species are included whose distribution is restricted to Lake Tanganyika. Two further representatives of this genus have very recently been discovered by ornamental fish exporters in Zambia. These in fact appear to be new and undescribed species. Why this small genus has become amazingly popular amongst aquarists is based on the fact that all its representatives are ideal fishes for the aquarium.

▶ *Julidochromis dickfeldi*
STAECK, 1975

The discovery of this small Cichlid happened in January 1975 when a group of

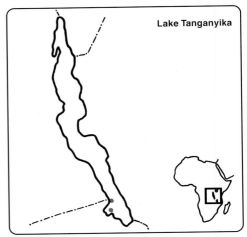

Localities of *Julidochromis dickfeldi*

German aquarists travelled to the south of Lake Tanganyika in order to study the natural habitats of aquarium-fishes. *Julidochromis dickfeldi* reaches a maximum size of eleven centimetres. However, the specimens observed in the lake were usually smaller

Male of *Julidochromis dickfeldi*

than ten centimetres. There is no obvious difference between males and females so that an identification of the sexes is hardly possible. A certain determination is only possible by observing a spawning act. *J. dickfeldi* is the only member of the genus which has an orange-brown ground-colouration and further differs by having an especially high dorsal fin.

The

natural habitat

of this Cichlid appears to exclusively lie in the southwestern corner of Lake Tanganyika. The only known collecting sites are on Zambian territory, i.e. on the northern border of the Sumbu National Park, and in neighbouring Zaïre. There, the fish are found above rocky ground and boulders. It appears that they prefer depths between two and six metres. They attach to a specific site where a breeding cave forms the centre of a territory. It is usually a horizontal or vertical rock crevice with a width of two or three centimetres.

The fish avoid the free water, but always stay close to the ground. At the slightest disturbance they disappear between the rocks. Catching them is therefore a matter of great effort and time consuming. It is thus one of the reasons why *Julidochromis* is imported very rarely and in small numbers.

The smaller species of *Julidochromis* are amongst other reasons ideal fishes for the aquarium because their

care

can be successful in a tank of only half a metre in length if certain preconditions are met. It however also requires a harmonic pair under these circumstances.

Opportunities for more detailed and interesting studies are obviously given in an aquarium of one and a half metres in length. This also enables the husbandry of several pairs together or the simultaneous keeping of other Cichlids from the rubble or rocky littoral of Lake Tanganyika. Appropriate

company fishes are species of the genera *Tropheus, Chalinochromis, Telmatochromis,* and small *Neolamprologus.*

The naturally decorated aquarium will provide numerous narrow crevices between stone-plates and rocks which may serve the *Julidochromis* as breeding sites and sanctuaries. The ground should consist of sand or fine gravel if possible. Apart from algae, the natural biotope of this fish is free of plants. Nevertheless it is possible to green the aquarium, and since *Julidochromis* even leaves the softest shoots alone, one may choose from the full range of available plants. It is notwithstanding advisable to preferably select those plants which either grow low or anchor themselves on the rocks in the aquarium.

In nature, *J. dickfeldi* exclusively feeds on small items such as small insect larvae, snails, and shrimps. Thus, *Daphnia* and White Mosquito-larvae (*Corethra*) are ideal food-items. Newly imported specimens usually refuse flake-food, but after an adjustment period, which might take up to half a year, TetraMin and TetraCichlid are readily accepted.

As already indicated above, a harmonic pair can also be brought to

breeding

in a relatively small aquarium. On the other hand, good breeding results can also be achieved in a naturally decorated community tank. The husbandry in a small aquarium is a problem in so far that all *Julidochromis* react very sensitive to even the slightest disturbance. It is typical for these Cichlids that proven breedingpairs which regularly have reared their offspring in an example-giving manner in the past, suddenly and apparently spontaneously begin to engage in vicious fights if there is any change in the aquarium. Even a simple exchange of water can be the stimulus for such fights which unfortunately usually result in the death of the subordinate specimen.

All *Julidochromis* are cave brooders. Preferred spawning sites are horizontal,

Nkamba Bay in the south of Lake Tanganyika. On this spot, Cichlids of the genera *Chalinochromis*, *Eretmodus*, *Julidochromis*, *Lamprologus*, and *Tropheus* were found.

but also vertical rock crevices, which offer just enough space for the specimens to swim in. In horizontal caves the spawning does not take place on the bottom, but always on the ceiling.

The fry is cared for in a parental family-structure where both the male and the female have more or less the same tasks. A bonding appears to develop between the reproduction partners which however does not seem to be as tight as in the case of West African Cichlids.

Sometimes a group of three is observed under aquarium conditions when a juvenile grows up and reaches maturity and is still tolerated in the territory of the parents. This behaviour may however be a result of the limited space in an aquarium since it has never been observed in the natural environment.

In comparison with West African cave brooders, the parental care of *Julidochromis* appears to be much less intense. The parental specimens spend relatively little attention to the clutch. This impression is supported by the fact that the juveniles are not kept in a school guided by the mother and the father, but are individualists. Thus it is no surprise that keepers of these species did not even notice that their specimens had spawned and were highly surprised when they suddenly discovered fairly large juveniles swimming through the aquarium.

J. dickfeldi is not especially productive. A clutch hardly ever contains more than forty eggs. They have a greyish green colouration, and at a water-temperature of 28 °C the larvae hatch after 60 hours. The freshly hatched larvae are usually spat against the ceiling by the parents where they attach to with the assistance of the glue-glands on the head.

Approximately on the seventh day after spawning, the juveniles begin to swim along the walls and the ceiling of the spawning-cave. Having a length of about three millimetres they are tiny, and for their rearing one thus requires very small food. The nauplii of the Brine Shrimp *Artemia salina*, MikroMin, or finely crushed TetraMin have been proven to be of the right size. If kept in a community tank, there is no need to feed the young fish separately as enough tiny food-particles remain from feeding the other fishes.

Provided with sufficient quantities of food, the juveniles may have grown to some twenty millimetres after three weeks. Thereafter, they keep on growing relatively slow. On reaching approximately three centimetres the parents begin to drive them out of their territory.

Aquarists occasionally complain about the species of *Julidochromis* not producing as many eggs as other species; a clutch often contains only ten eggs. In this connection an observation is of interest which could be confirmed by studies in the natural biotope. These Cichlids have two different reproduction strategies.

Firstly, they may produce clutches in quick succession and be constantly engaged in breeding. Often, there are only ten days between two successive clutches. In this modus, the number of juveniles is very small. On the other hand, the clutch may consist of a higher number of eggs and consequently the time between the individual spawnings is considerably longer; it may be up to half a year.

To date it is unknown which factors determine the *Julidochromis* species to switch from one reproduction modus to the other. Reasons might be amongst others an increasing or decreasing availability of food or a decreasing or increasing population density. In this connection it is interesting that there are also a number of species of *Neolamprologus*, e.g. *N. savornyi*, which have extremely small clutches, but which permanently spawn at surprisingly short intervals.

◗ *Julidochromis ornatus*
BOULENGER, 1898
(Northern Colour variety)

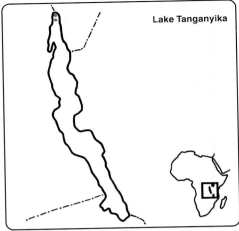

Localities of the northern variety of *Julidochromis ornatus*

was first imported as aquarium fish in 1958. Since then, only small numbers of individuals were imported on rare occasions and thus many of the presently kept specimens still originate from these initial imports. It is therefore of no surprise that certain degeneration symptoms have occasionally been observed in this species.

Julidochromis ornatus may reach a maximum length of close to eight centimetres. The Northern Colour-morph portrayed here has two brownish black longitudinal stripes on the golden yellow ground colouration of the lateral sides. A third stripe runs along the base of the dorsal fin. In contrast, the Southern Colour morph which originates from the vicinity of Mupulungu has an ivory body-colouration instead of a golden yellow one. Males and females look the same.

Julidochromis ornatus (northern variety)

The natural habitat

of the northern form lies on the northwestern shore of Lake Tanganyika. Records have been made from the villages of Uvira, Kalungwe, and Kashekezi in northern Zaïre. Here, the fish have preferably been found a depths between two and four metres. They exclusively inhabit the rubble- and rocky littoral of the lake.

Care

Keeping this species may either occur in a community aquarium or in pairs in a smaller tank of at least fifty centimetres. Positive experiences were made when the species was kept together with mouthbrooding species of *Tropheus*. Inhabitants of the upper rubble- or rocky littoral, e.g. small species of *Neolamprologus* or the Goby Cichlids, also make appropriate company fishes. The community aquarium should especially emulate the natural environment as closely as possible so that the specimens have a sufficient number of hiding places to choose from. It should be pointed out that *J. ornatus even* leaves delicate shoots of

Larvae of *Julidochromis ornatus* on the fifth day after fertilization of the eggs

plants alone. Since the fish has a very small mouth, its diet should consist of Daphnia, small insectlarvae, and flake-food.

The

breeding

has frequently been successful and does not cause any problems when slightly hard and alkaline or neutral water is available.

As is the case with other *Julidochromis* this species is also a specialized cave brooder which cares for the offspring in a parental family.

The rocky littoral of Lake Tanganyika is the biotope for the species of *Julidochromis*.

▶ *Julidochromis regani*
POLL, 1942

may grow up to fifteen centimetres in its natural biotope and thus is the largest representative of its genus. Since there is no sexual dimorphism, males and females can hardly be distinguished. However, at reaching a length of approximately ten centimetres, the form of the urogenital papilla is constantly visible and provides usable information. Whilst it is short and pointed forward in females, it is up to four millimetres long and directed backwards in males even outside spawning activities.

Several colour morphs are known from *Julidochromis regani* which differ with regard to the ratio of light to dark portions of the colour-pattern. Usually, the fish has a pattern of four dark stripes on the yellowish body, whilst some varieties appear to have light stripes on a dark background colour-

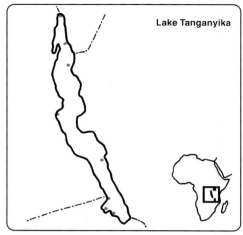

Localities of *Julidochromis regani*

ation. Specimens from certain localities have distinct dark markings in their fins, whilst these are almost colourless in others.

Male of *Julidochromis regani*

The

natural habitat

of the pretty variety shown here in a photograph lies in Burundi. According to data published by BRICHARD (1978), this colour morph is only found in a very small area in the northern tip of Lake Tanganyika near the town Bujumbura. Due to the fact that the dark sections of the colouration are very broad, the fish appear to have a pattern of light yellow longitudinal stripes on a brownish black ground-colour.

Julidochromis regani is native to the rubble- and rocky littoral. Amongst its relatives in this genus this species has the widest distribution and is therefore frequently encountered. It does not only occur in the north (Burundi, Tanzania) and in the south (Zambia), but it was also recorded from the central west coast (Zaïre). I furthermore found this species on the central east coast north of Kipili in Tanzania. In the vicinity of Kigoma it occurs in a colour morph which appears intermediate between *J. marlieri* and *J. regani*.

In their natural environment, this Cichlid preys upon a variety of micro-organisms which they find amongst the lawn of algae. Feeding newly imported specimens is therefore often a problem since they refuse flake-food, but only accept small live shrimps and insect larvae. After a period of adjustment which usually takes half a year, they accept all common types of food.

With the precondition of having a harmonic pair which one wants to keep on its own, the

care

requires an aquarium of approximately half a metre in length. Basically, the keeping in a large community tank is recommendable where the specimens share their environment with species of *Neolamprologus*, *Chalinochromis*, or Goby Cichlids. In any case the aquarium should be decorated according to nature.

Many crevices and gaps between the rocks are necessary for

breeding

as they are required for spawning and to rear the fry. These sanctuaries however also serve to define borders of territories and enable subordinate specimens to retreat out of sight of superior opponents.

As there are no significant differences amongst the species of *Julidochromis* with regard to the sexual and breeding behaviour, reference is made to the data provided in the account of *J. dickfeldi*. It is important to bear in mind that even pairs which had lived together in perfect harmony for a long time, may suddenly and for no apparent reason begin to quarrel and temporarily engage in vicious fights.

Julidochromis regani in its natural environment; the rubble-littoral in Sumbu National Park (Zambia) at two metres depth

◆ *Julidochromis transcriptus*
MATTHES, 1959

is known to the aquaristic since the early sixties. As the subsequent few specimens were not imported before 1979, it is not really a surprise that degeneration symptoms have been observed in some aquarium populations which primarily affects the colouration. Well marked specimens resemble the import-male in the photograph and have four to five narrow ivory- to cream-white transversal stripes on a pitch black background colour. As males and females are identic, determination of the sex is a difficult task. *J. transcriptus* is the smallest representative of the genus with the maximum length of this species being 6 cm in males. Females are usually distinctly smaller than males.

The natural distribution

of this Cichlid appears to be greatly restricted. The sole locality known to date

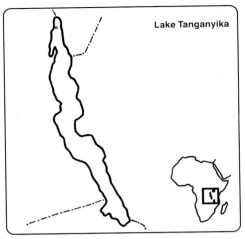

Locality of *Julidochromis transcriptus*

lies in the northwestern corner of Lake Tanganyika in Zaïre and extends between the villages of Luhanga and Makobola.

The fish exclusively inhabits the rubble- and rocky littoral and prefers depths between one and five metres. However,

Male of *Julidochromis transcriptus*

scuba-divers have occasionally observed it at depths of fifteen or even thirty metres.

Food is primarily found amongst the lawn of algae. Examinations of stomach-contents revealed that, besides algae, small shrimps of various species and mainly small insect larvae are preyed upon.

The natural

care

takes place in an aquarium that provides the fish with numerous narrow crevices and niches amongst respective rock construc-tions which they can use as spawning-caves and for sanctuary. Although this pretty Cichlid can of course be kept in pairs in rela-tively small aquaria of around fifty centime-tres in length, a tank with a length of one and a half metres where it is housed together with other Cichlids from the rocky shore-zone of Lake Tanganyika should rather be considered. This manner of keeping is more interesting. Such an aquarium could be fur-nished with Goby Cichlids, and species of

Tropheus or small *Neolamprologus*. Even *J. dickfeldi* and *J. regani* can easily be kept with *J. transcriptus* in a larger tank.

Although no higher aquatic plants occur in the natural biotope of this species, the aquarium can be decorated with plants since not even the softest shoots are touched. Newly imported specimens will accept flake-food only after a longer period of adjustment. On the other hand, *Daphnia* and mosquito larvae are immediately and readily taken.

As in the case of all other species of *Juli-dochromis, J. transcriptus* is a cave brooder which cares for and protects its fry in a biparental family.

Since its

breeding

does not differ from that of the other rep-resentatives of its genus, reference is made to the hints given for the breeding of *J. dick-feldi*.

The harbour of Ujiji (Tanzania) is situated on a swampy part of the coast.

◗ *Julidochromis* sp.
"Gombi"

This scientifically undescribed representative of the genus *Julidochromis* was only discovered in 1989. It is one of the smallest species in this genus and can be regarded fully grown at 6 cm. The body is marked with a fairly regular pattern of six alternating transversal bands of beige and brownish black colouring respectively. A conspicuous yellow colour-zone runs along the base of the dorsal fin. The pectoral fins are yellow whereas all other fins are mainly brownish black. The sexes hardly differ from one another except that larger males have a longer and more slender urogenital papilla.

The

natural habitat

of this fish lies in the southeastern corner of Lake Tanganyika. According to information

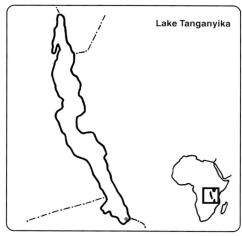

Locality of *Julidochromis* sp. "Gombi"

obtained from exporters this species inhabits a very small area west of Chituta Bay. They exclusively occur on shore-zones with rocky ground or boulders where they live in the upper littoral.

Julidochromis sp. "Gombi"

The Genus

Labeotropheus

was described by AHL in 1927. It accommodates two species which resembles each other closely and can only be told apart by their body-shapes. *Labeotropheus trewavasae* is slender and elongate whereas *L. fuelleborni* is more stout and high-backed. Both belong to the Mbuna-cichlids which means that they feed on the lawn of algae and micro-organisms that cover stones and rocks in the upper shore-zone.

The species of *Labeotropheus* have adapted to their environment in a very special manner. Their extremely low-set mouth enables them to graze on the algae-lawn in a more or less normal swimming position. Other Mbuna-cichlids in contrast need to almost stand on the head to feed. The genus *Labeotropheus* is endemic to Lake Malawi.

◆ *Labeotropheus fuelleborni*
AHL, 1927

generally reaches a length of twelve centimetres, but may, under favourable aquarium-conditions, also grow to just under fifteen centimetres.

The species has a remarkable polychromatism, which means that specimens from even the same collecting site may be coloured completely different. Males of the most common variety are bright light blue whilst their females are greyish blue.

Besides this "normal" variety, there is the so-called orange blotch morph, which has a pattern of irregularly arranged black spots and speckles on an ivory-coloured to yellowish orange ground. It consists almost exclusively of females.

The extremely rare males of the so-called OB morph are recognizable by a blueish tinge which becomes especially obvious during courtship.

Male of *Labeotropheus fuelleborni*, Mbenji variety

The
natural habitat

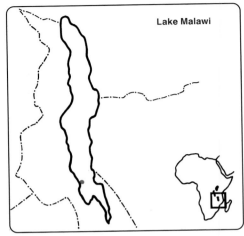

Lake Malawi

of this Cichlid is the rubble- and rocky littoral of Lake Malawi. The fish is especially
common in the southwestern part of the
lake whereas they do not seem to inhabit the
northeastern shore in Tanzania.

The species occurs in quite a variety of
different colour races. The photograph of
the male with its golden yellow blotch on
the flank shows a specimen from the littoral
of Mbenji Islands. Specimens from the
Maleri Islands are in contrast uniformly
blue. In males from the vicinity of Cape
Maclear, the ventral fins and posterior portions of the dorsal and anal fins are yellowish orange. A particularly beautiful reddish
orange dorsal fin marks males from the
Chindunga Rocks near the village of Chipoka whilst specimens from Cinyankwazi
have an almost black dorsal fin. Males from
Likoma Island are uniformly light blue.

Locality of the Mbenji variety

Care

As the fish do not make great demands on
the water chemistry, keeping this Cichlid is
easy if attention is given to some basics. If
possible, *L. fuelleborni* should not be kept

Labeotropheus fuelleborni, female of the orange blotch morph

on its own, but in a spacious community aquarium of approximately one and a half metres in length.

As the males constantly pursue the females, the keeping of only one pair is out of the question; two to three females are required. On the other hand, two males can only be kept together in exceptionally large tanks because of the high degree of intraspecific aggression.

Appropriate company fishes are found amongst the Mbuna-cichlids of the genera *Pseudotropheus, Melanochromis,* or *Labidochromis* and other hardy Haplochromines. The natural decoration of the aquarium will utilize rocks and stone-plates which are arranged in such a way that they provide numerous niches and caves along the rear wall of the tank. The substrate should consist of sand or fine gravel.

Although the natural biotope of this fish is bare of higher plants, the aquarium may be greened. The choice is however limited to sturdy robust species, such as the West African *Anubias* or the Asian fern *Microsorium pteropus,* since the fish permanently abrate the plants and rocks with their teeth in search of food.

Despite *L. fuelleborni* being a highly adapted foodspecialist, its feeding is no matter of concern. *Daphnia,* insect larvae, TetraMin, and TetraPhyll are willingly accepted. Otherwise, ox-heart and food with small contents of fibres like earthworms are inappropriate for this Cichlid. Their usage should therefore be limited.

The

breeding

preferably occurs in the community aquarium. The mother specimen with the fry in her mouth is then isolated when the larval development is close to finalization. *L. fuelleborni* is a specialized mouthbrooder which rears its offspring in a mother-family. This fish is agamous, i.e. there is no bonding between the reproduction partners. The males court any female ready to spawn and

by trembling and leading try to lure them into their territories.

A flat stone inside a cave or at another concealed site is the preferred spawning site. The female usually lays egg by egg and immediately takes them into the mouth. Thereafter it follows the male with the head close to his anal region sucking up the sperm to fertilize the eggs. At a water-temperature of approximately 26 °C it may be expected that the juveniles leave the mouth of the mother after about twenty days for the first time. At this stage they measure already almost ten millimetres and are fairly independent. They are easily reared on a diet of selected small *Daphnia* and crushed flake-food.

Since they have inherited the instinctive behaviour which ensures the survival in a densely populated habitat, a few juveniles also grow up in a community aquarium. As soon as the mouthbrooding care of the mother ceases, they seek cover in individual rock crevices which then become the centres of the territory defended against all other siblings.

Males of *Labeotropheus fuelleborni* engaged in mouth-tearing. Rocky littoral of Dombwe Island at three metres depth.

The Genus Labidochromis
TREWAVAS, 1935

Thoroughly revised by LEWIS in 1982, this genus belongs to the taxonomically most completely investigated cladistic groups of Lake Malawi. Presently, it holds eighteen scientifically described species which are complemented by further species of doubtful status due to insufficient descriptions and some undescribed forms which have primarily been found on the northeastern shore of the lake in Tanzania during the past few years. As far as ichthyology is concerned, this part belongs to the most incompletely researched ones.

This genus is of special importance for the aquaristic pursuit as most of the members of *Labidochromis* have an extraordinarily small adult-size of just seven to eight centimetres. They can therefore be properly kept in less spacious aquaria. Some species furthermore have very splendid colour patterns which, in contrast to other Mbuna-cichlids, are present in both sexes. Bright tones of blue, but also white and yellow are colours commonly found in this genus. Despite these features, only a few representatives of this cladistic group are really common amongst aquarists, one reason being the few imports of most of the species.

All species of *Labidochromis* belong to the Mbuna-cichlids, which means that they feed on the lawn of algae of Lake Malawi. They differ from other Cichlids of this ecological group through the arrangement of teeth. In most of the members of the genus *Labidochromis* the teeth in the outer central area of the jaws are not two-apexed but comparatively long and tapering to a single point. It is typical for some species that they preferably inhabit the zone of shallow water near the shore whereas other prefer the lower rocky zone and thus are difficult to observe and catch. The members of the second mentioned group are little attached to a specific locality and migrate through wide areas.

▶ Labidochromis caeruleus
FRYER, 1959

The first specimens of the marvellously yellow coloured morph of *Labidochromis caeruleus* reached German pet-shops in 1989. Curiously enough they did not originate from Malawi but from Burundi where a local catcher and exporter of Tanganyika-cichlids had bred them in large numbers.

In the literature this Cichlid was first mentioned by RIBBINK and coauthors (1983) who considered it to be a rare colour morph of *Labidochromis caeruleus*. Although this hypothesis has not yet been dealt with truly scientifically, many points of view seem to support this presumption. Firstly, both forms have exactly the same colour pattern with one exception, i.e. the ground colouration is white in the form described as *Labidochromis caeruleus* and not yellow. In courting males, the white is overlain by a blueish tinge. Still, both colour morphs have a more or less identic distribution, and intermediates between both colour morphs are found in the natural biotope. On occasion of a joint dive a few kilometres north of Nkhata Bay where we observed and photographed the white morph of *Labidochromis caeruleus*, BRENNER saw a white specimen which had isolated bright yellow coloured patches on the back.

The yellow morph is bright lemon-yellow on the head, the entire body, and the caudal fin. The dorsal fin is marked with a broad black longitudinal band below a narrow yellow margin. The outer part of the anal fin is also coloured black. Certain inconspicuous differences exist regarding the colouration of males and females. Courting males in their territories have a dark, usually dirty brownish mask below the eye between upper lip and the edge of the preoperculum. They furthermore have pitch black ventral fins whereas those of the females are yellow. Under aquarium conditions, males grow up to approximately eight, females up to seven centimetres.

The

natural habitat

of *Labidochromis caeruleus* lies in the lower area of the rocky littoral. Although the fish has also been observed at lower depths in the transitory zone from sandy to rocky ground (RIBBINK et al. 1983), it is more common at depths of ten to forty metres in rocky regions of the shore. Localities for the white morph of *Labidochromis caeruleus* are known from the northwest of the lake between Ruarwe and Chirombo Point. However, the yellow morph has only been recorded from the north of the range with the southernmost collecting point being Lion's Cove.

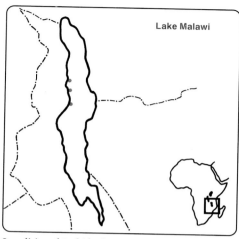

Localities of *Labidochromis caeruleus*

Care

For the successful keeping of this hardy Cichlid an aquarium with a floor-space of 100 by 50 centimetres is sufficient. It should be decorated to emulate a section of the rocky littoral and enable the specimens to define territories.

Breeding

Labidochromis caeruleus is a maternal mouth-breeder with no bonding between male and female.

Yellow morph of *Labidochromis caeruleus*

◆ *Labidochromis chisumulae*
LEWIS, 1982

These small Cichlids certainly rank amongst the most colourful representatives of this genus. Imported male specimens usually measure up to seven centimetres, but may reach up to eight centimetres in the aquarium. Females remain approximately one centimetre smaller.

Courting males display a bright light blue ground colouration. Up to eight black transversal bands cross over the body between the posterior edge of the operculum and the base of the tail of which the last three are reduced to indications. A broad pitch-black band obliquely runs from the nape through the eye to the angle of the mouth. Another black stripe also begins on the nape and ends on the upper angle of the operculum. The dorsal fin has a light blue margin, is coloured pitch black in the spinous section, and blue in its posterior portion. The ventral fins and

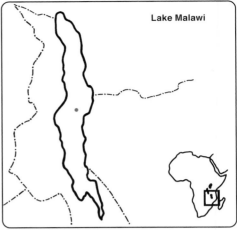

Locality of *Labidochromis chisumulae*

the anterior section of the anal fin are blackish with the posterior portion of the anal fin being marked with up to three orange egg dummies.

Male of *Labidochromis chisumulae*

The sex of adult specimens can be distinguished fairly easily by the colouration. Females lack the blue in the background colouration and are more whitish with the distinct black banded pattern of the males being rarely displayed and if so greatly reduced.

The

natural habitat

of *Labidochromis chisumulae* is the upper rocky littoral. Here, the fish was most frequently observed at depths between eight and twenty-five metres (LEWIS 1982). It belong to the non-territorial representatives of the genus and, while in search of food, restlessly swim around alone or more rarely in small groups and roam fair distances. They primarily feed on small invertebrates including crustaceans and the larvae of mosquitos and other insects.

The distribution of *Labidochromis chisumulae* is extremely small and — as the species name indicates — restricted to the small island Chisumulu.

Care

An aquarium with a floor-space of 100×50 cm is sufficient for this fairly small species. It should however not be kept on its own, but together with other small Mbuna-cichlids from Lake Malawi. The presence of other fishes is a good measure to considerably reduce the natural intraspecific aggression. Other species of *Labidochromis* as well as representatives of the genera *Iodotropheus* and *Labeotropheus* make suitable company fishes. The decoration of the aquarium requires thoroughly rinsed coarse sand, rocks, and stone-plates which are arranged in a manner that emulates the rocky littoral with all its variety of crevices and grottos. Instead of a pair, one or two males should be kept together with several females.

Breeding

Labidochromis chisumulae is an ovophile maternal mouthbrooder. The fairly large juveniles are already capable of feeding on selected small micro-shrimps when they leave the mouth of the mother.

Rocky shore of Likoma Island (Lake Malawi)

The Genus Lepidiolamprologus

PELLEGRIN, 1903

This genus was established as early as the start of this century, temporarily discarded as invalid, and eventually revived by the Belgian ichthyologist POLL in 1986 in order to accommodate six species which were assigned to the genus *Lamprologus* until then. They are united by the feature of having numerous remarkably small scales.

◆ *Lepidiolamprologus nkambae*

(STAECK, 1978)

This conspicuously coloured Cichlid was discovered on occasion of a six week collecting survey in the upper littoral of the southern part of Lake Tanganyika in Zambia in April 1975. It was immediately noticed during underwater studies by the author due to its unusual appearance. Although the species was spotted repeatedly, only one specimen could eventually be captured which later served for the description of the species.

The very slender fish has a mustard-brown to blackish brown ground colour and a pattern of four to five narrow, irregular zigzag-lines which have a whitish green

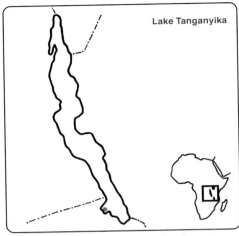

Locality of *Lepidiolamprologus nkambae*

shine mainly on the lower half of the body. The specimens observed all measured around fifteen centimetres. It is however possible that the maximum length is greater, since the closely related species *L. elongatus* reaches up to twenty centimetres.

The

natural habitat

of this fish is the rocky littoral. Here, it resides close to the bottom. Their slow-moving and lurking behaviour with frequent motionless breaks of approximately one

Lepidiolamprologus nkambae

minute is noteworthy. It is to be presumed that the fish has a predatory ecology and grasps its prey in a flash-fast manner. The depth of the water where it was observed ranged from three to six metres. It is however possible that the preferred levels are the deeper zones. This would be an explanation for the rare encounters with this fish.

The few known localities of this species all lie in the extreme south of Lake Tanganyika in Zambia.

Care

Keeping this interesting Cichlid in captivity is not connected to specific problems. Being an ambuscader, the fish is no vivid swimmer, but calm and despite its size requires little space. Since *Lepidiolamprologus nkambae* is an inhabitant of the rocky littoral, the aquarium should be decorated with stone-plates and rocks in such a manner that the fish can choose from a variety of sanctuaries. This Cichlid is tolerant towards other fishes, but it should always be borne in mind that it has a predatory ecology and is able to down fairly large food-items with its deeply grooved mouth. Its company fishes should therefore be selected from larger species, e. g. the bigger members of *Neolamprologus*.

Breeding

has repeatedly been successful. A clutch of this very productive cave brooder may consist of several hundred eggs.

Rubble zone of Lake Tanganyika

The Genus Limnochromis

REGAN, 1920

is endemic to Lake Tanganyika and originally held eleven species. However, being a very heterogenous group, species have repeatedly been extracted and transferred to other genera during the eighties. POLL (1986) grouped these in the tribe Limnochromini. At present, three species have remained in the genus *Limnochromis*, i.e. *L. auritus*, *L. abeelei*, and *L. staneri*, of which only the first mentioned is known to the aquarists.

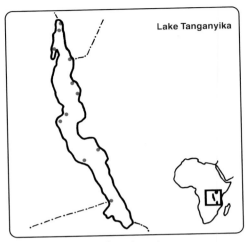

Localities of *Limnochromis auritus*

▶ *Limnochromis auritus*

(BOULENGER, 1901)

This Cichlid from Lake Tanganyika has been kept in aquaria in Germany since the early seventies, but is rarely imported. It reaches a length of twenty centimetres, but despite its attractive appearance and interesting behaviour it has not gained common popularity.

In the region of the back, this fish is coloured greyish brown whereas the belly is whitish. These background colours are overlain by a metallic gleam which assumes rosy to violet tones on the upper half of the body and golden to silvery tones on the lower. The flanks are marked with four broad, dark, transversal bands of which the

Limnochromis auritus

first lies immediately behind the gill-cover and the last on the base of the tail. Below the hind edge of the dorsal fin there usually is an indication of a fifth band. Three to four longitudinal stripes of silvery shining scales extend from the edge of the gill-cover to the base of the caudal fin. All unpairy fins are patterned with shining light blue speckles.

Since there are no distinct feature in the appearance of males and females, the identification of sexes is a very difficult task. Fairly reliable results can only be achieved by comparing the urogenital papilla which is slightly larger in female specimens.

The

natural habitat

of *Limnochromis auritus* lies in the lower shore-zone above sandy and muddy ground. The fish appears to prefer levels between thirty and fifty metres in depth, but has been recorded at depths of more than one hundred metres. Studies on stomach-contents (POLL, 1956) showed that snails and small shrimp-species of the *Cyclops*-group are the most important sources of food for this Cichlid.

The distribution of *Limnochromis auritus* extends over the entire Lake Tanganyika with localities known from the north (Burundi), the east (Tanzania), the west (Zaïre), and the southwest (Zambia).

Care

Provided with rather hard water with pH-values at alkaline levels, the maintenance of this Cichlid is generally easy. Accounting for its maximum length, a spacious aquarium with a floor-space of at least 150 × 50 centimetres becomes a necessity. The rear wall should be furnished with rock-constructions amongst which the fish find several caves for hiding.

Taking the conditions from the natural environment of this fish into consideration, the aquarium should not be furnished with gravel but with coarse sand. During the pro-

cess of decoration one should make provisions for the species' peculiarity to often dig in the ground and excavate large pits.

Since *Limnochromis auritus* willingly accepts all common types of food, a varying diet does not require much effort. It should however be borne in mind that the large fish needs a fair quantity of food.

Reports on a successful

breeding

of this Cichlid under aquarium conditions are extraordinarily rare. The reason for this is presumably the fact that *Limnochromis auritus* is not imported often and then only in small numbers. The determination of the sex is also a big problem.

Limnochromis auritus belongs to the small number of biparental mouthbrooders of Lake Tanganyika. Other Cichlids of this group, e.g. the Goby Cichlids of the tribe Eretmodini, engage in consecutive care for the fry, i.e. the female takes over the first part and the male the rest. Yet other species do this alternatingly by recurrently passing the eggs or larvae on to the partner.

In contrast, male and female of this species have a simultaneous mouthbrooding biology. Both parental specimens usually take a share of the eggs into the mouth for incubation immediately after they have been laid. Subsequently it happens increasingly often that only one fish carries the whole fry (comp. e.g. BAASCH 1987). Depending on the water-temperature, the juveniles may be released from the mouth after nearly two weeks. Male and female then continue their joint mouthbrooding care for approximately another two weeks.

Although the juveniles are initially fairly tiny, they can easily be reared with newly hatched nauplii of the Brine Shrimp.

The Genus Melanochromis

was established by the ichthyologist TREWA-VAS in 1935 and redefined by her in 1984. On this occasion, she also followed the suggestions of other authors and pointed out the colour-pattern as the major identification feature. RIBBINK and co-authors (1982) included fifteen species in the *Melanochromis* species-complex of which only seven are scientifically described. This group is supplemented by another three species described by JOHNSON in the seventies whose status is uncertain due to scant descriptions.

All *Melanochromis* are slender, elongate fishes whose colour pattern stands out through conspicuous longitudinal stripes. Males have light stripes on a dark ground colour whereas females and juveniles have dark strips on light ground.

Within the genus, two groups can be distinguished. The first incorporates small to moderately sized species with a narrow mouth and a short roundish head. The second unites distinctly larger species with a large, deeply grooved mouth.

Judging from morphological traits, the species of *Melanochromis* appear to be closely allied to the genus *Pseudotropheus* and are thus rightfully included in the group of Mbuna-cichlids. Observations in captivity and while diving in the natural habitats showed that they embody a completely different ecological type.

In contrast to *Pseudotropheus* they are far less specialized users of the lawn of algae. The point-headed species apparently rather feed on small shrimps, insect larvae, and even juvenile fishes. This ecology obviously contributes to the particularity that they are less attached to a specific location and instead constantly roam through fairly wide territories which are viciously defended against conspecifics. The severe intraspecific aggression of this Cichlid is naturally a disturbing factor in the aquarium.

Unfortunately, not only the males are completely belligerent amongst each other, the females are also extremely unsocial and fight bloody battles under captive circumstances. Although the species of *Melanochromis* display striking colour patterns, the aforementioned reasons make them no fishes recommendable for the beginner.

The negative behavioural attributes of all *Melanochromis* become even more disturbing the smaller the available space is. The long-term husbandry of these fishes therefore calls for aquaria as large as possible.

Rocky zone on the southwestern shore of Lake Malawi (Cape Maclear)

◗ *Melanochromis auratus*
(BOULENGER, 1897)

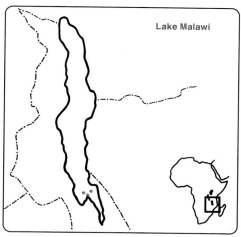

Localities of *Melanochromis auratus*

is undoubtedly one of the most commonly known Cichlids of Lake Malawi. When the species was first imported in the early sixties, the significant colour pattern of the females and the juveniles initiated thrilling excitement. At this time, the Cichlid was still assigned to the genus *Pseudotropheus*. In the meantime, it has become fairly silent around this undoubtedly very pretty fish. Surely the subsequent import of even more conspicuously coloured species has contributed to this. On the other hand, it was commonly realized that it is by no means an easy-to-keep species.

Melanochromis auratus reaches an approximate length of ten centimetres. Males and females have very different colour patterns. Females and juveniles display two pitch black longitudinal stripes on a cadmium-yellow to silvery white ground colour laterally. Males are in contrast mainly black with two whitish green to greenish golden longitudinal stripes on the flanks. This colour pattern is assumed at an approximate length of six centimetres, i.e. when they reach maturity. If an adult specimen of the same sex is present, the

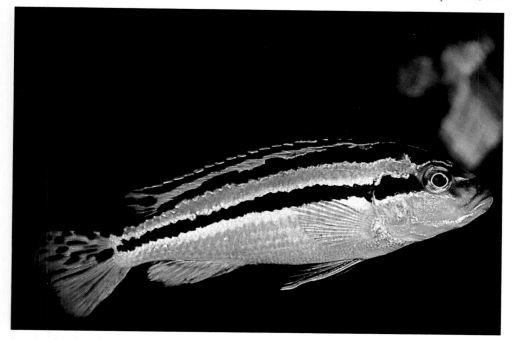

Female of *Melanochromis auratus*

beginning of the colour-change is postponed for a surprisingly long period of time. In such case the specimen "camouflages" itself more or less as a female and thus prevents to be identified as a rival by the stronger male.

On the other hand, old females often assume a very dark colouration and may closely resemble males at the first glance. It is typical for such dark specimens that they are remarkably aggressive towards conspecifics. The physiological and behavioural aspects of this phenomenon in this and other species of *Melanochromis,* and one species of *Pseudotropheus* too, are an enigma to date.

The

natural habitat

of *M. auratus* is the rubble- and rocky zone. The presently known localities concentrate in the south of Lake Malawi. Specimens from the eastern shore (Mozambique) are duller in colour than those from the west coast. Amongst its genus, this species belongs to the forms with a small mouth and a short head. The major source of food is the lawn of algae which the fish either bites or rips off with a quick jerk of the head.

Care

The perfect conditions for keeping this fish definitely require a large aquarium of at least one and a half metres in length. Due to the extremely developed intraspecific aggression of this species, specimens cannot be kept on their own. Their husbandry appears to be only possible in a naturally decorated community aquarium where the presence of Cichlids of other genera suppresses the instinctive aggression towards fellow specimens.

As is the case in the majority of mouthbrooding Cichlids, the males of *M. auratus* need to be kept with a harem. Since the courtship site is ferociously defended even against fishes of other species, company

Melanochromis auratus in three metres depth in the natural setting

fishes must be chosen from fairly robust species which stand a chance to resist the *Melanochromis.* Appropriate options are the large species of *Nimbochromis* and *Pseudotropheus,* e.g. *P. lombardoi* or *P. zebra* and *P. elongatus.*

The decoration of the tank requires pieces and plates of rock which are arranged to form caves and alcoves particularly on the rear wall and thus emulate the situation found in the natural habitat of Mbuna-cichlids. Since *M. auratus* is plant-tolerant, plants can be used for decoration although these do not occur in the natural environment. They should not substantially restrain the available swimming-space. Feeding this species is no problem and all commonly used types of food are accepted. It should of course be as varying as possible and therefore consist of assorted kinds of flake-food, small shrimp species, and insect-larvae.

The

breeding

of this Cichlid is most promising in the community aquarium described above.

M. auratus is a specialized mouthbrooder. The male chooses a spawning site which is usually a stone in a covered location.

Major elements of the male's courtship are trembling and leading. The fertilization of the eggs takes place in the mouth of the female where they are stored immediately after being laid.

At water-temperatures around 27 °C, the fry is cared for by the mother for approximately three weeks until they are released for the first time. This period of time may however be extended for a few days if the female feels molested by other fish and does not find an undisturbed site where it can spit out the juveniles without danger. Once the juveniles are released the maternal care ends soon. The young *M. auratus* are fairly independent, and apparently the instinct to return into the mouth of the mother is weakly developed. They soon find themselves adequate cavities for concealment which serve them as residential territories for the next days or weeks.

The behaviour of juvenile *M. auratus* thus obviously differs from that of other Haplochromines which are less independent and therefore need to rely more on the protection by the mother to survive.

Young Mbuna-cichlids therefore also grow up in a community aquarium. If it is intended to rear the entire fry, it is advisable to remove the mother after approximately two weeks of mouthbrooding care. Transferred to a separate tank, it then may finalize the breeding. The juveniles can be reared easily by feeding them selected small *Daphnia* and crushed flake-food.

Vegetated zone in Lake Malawi at three metres depth with *Hemitilapia oxyrhynchus*

◗ *Melanochromis chipokae*
JOHNSON, 1975

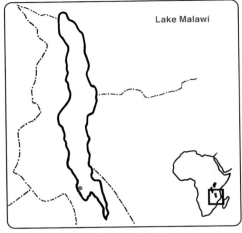

Lake Malawi

Locality of *Melanochromis chipokae*

may reach a body length of close to fourteen centimetres under aquarium conditions. The identification of the sexes is easy in the case of adult specimens as the species has a distinct sexual dichromatism. Males are mainly blueish black with two light blue longitudinal stripes on the upper half of the body. The same colourtone is found in the dorsal fin. In contrast, females and juveniles have two pitch black longitudinal stripes on an ochre or golden yellowish background colour. The species belongs to the *Melanochromis* with a pointed head and larger mouth.

The

natural distribution

of this species is very limited. The only locality known to date is the Chidunga Rocks, an underwater-reef near the village of Chipoka in the southwestern part of Lake Malawi. The fish is an inhabitant of the rocky littoral. Although the lawn of algae plays an important role regarding their resources of food, they are less specialized. The major prey should instead consist of various invertebrates, but also juveniles fishes.

Care

The can be problems with keeping this Cichlid for it appears to be possible only in a large community aquarium being about

Male of *Melanochromis chipokae*

one and a half metres in length. The fish can be fairly aggressive towards conspecifics as well as towards other species. This unpleasant attribute is quite disturbing in too small tanks, but in company of only a few other Cichlids and sufficient available space, the aggressive actions diminish to an acceptable measure. *M. chipokae* cannot be kept in pairs, but a male should have several females available. Company fishes need to be hardy Malawi-cichlids from the rocky zone and preferably be larger Mbuna-cichlids or species of *Nimbochromis.*

Since *M. chipokae* does not feed on plants, the aquarium can be planted. But the flora should be kept in proportion because the fish needs space for swimming and its natural biotope is not obstructed with plants. The most important items of decoration are pieces of rock and stone-plates which are used to emulate an underwater-reef with many crevices and alcoves. Along the back wall of the tank the rock construction should range up to just under the water surface.

If the above hints are paid attention, even the

breeding

is no problem. As in the case of other *Melanochromis,* it should be tried in the community aquarium. Shortly before the larval development of the fry is completed, the caring female should then be transferred to a separate tank where it can finalize its task undisturbed.

This Cichlid is also a specialized mouth-brooder which rears its offspring in a mother-family. At a temperature of approximately 26 °C, the larval development is completed after some three weeks. As soon as the juveniles have left the mouth of the mother they become independent and the care of the mother-specimen soon ceases. Due to the fact that the young *M. chipokae* are as large as all other Mbuna-cichlids, they are easily reared on a diet of selected small *Daphnia* and crushed flake-food.

In places, the population density of Mbuna-cichlids is surprisingly high (Yofu Rocks near Likoma Island, five metres deep).

◗ *Melanochromis* sp.
"lepidophage"

This scientifically undescribed Cichlid has been imported as ornamental fish since the mid-eighties. With regard to its body shape and colour pattern it is a typical representative of the genus. It has an elongate, laterally quite compressed body and is patterned with two dark longitudinal stripes on the flanks of which one runs along the back and the other extends from the hind edge of the eye to the base of the tail. The dorsal and the anal fins may be marked with a pale dark longitudinal band. Except for their whitish anterior edges the ventral fins are smoky dark grey. The caudal fin also often has a blackish submarginal banded pattern on the posterior edge. The anal fin is marked with usually three egg dummies which are bordered with black. The fish reaches a length of approximately twelve centimetres.

With a distinct sexual dichromatism present, the identification of the sexes is easy. Females, as well as juveniles, have a whitish ground colouration whereas males are col-

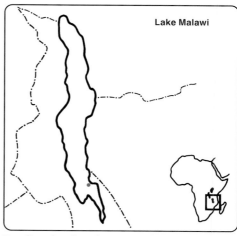

Locality of *Melanochromis* sp. "lepidophage"

oured bright light blue. The nape and shoulder region usually has a brass-coloured gleam. In dominant males the black stripes may completely disappear so that they eventually are uniformly light blue.

Male of *Melanochromis* sp. "lepidophage"

The

natural habitat

of *Melanochromis* sp. "lepidophage" is the transitory zone from rocky to sandy ground at depths up to ten metres. It seems that this Cichlid is endemic to a small area south of the village of Fort Maguire on the east coast. The only localities known to date are on the West Reef, an underwater-reef off Makanjila Point.

Interesting details on the ecology of this species were published by Ribbink and others (1983). According to them, this fish, in contrast to other species of *Melanochromis*, is not explicitly territorial, but lives socially in schools which may incorporate up to sixty specimens. Examinations of stomach contents undertaken by the aforementioned authors revealed that this Cichlid feeds on scales and apparently would attack large Haplochromines.

Care

Despite all expectations, the successful maintenance of this Cichlid turned out to be surprisingly easy. In comparison with other species of *Melanochromis,* which are not only aggressive towards conspecifics, this fish is pleasantly timid. It is noteworthy that it does not specialize on a certain type of prey, but willingly accepts of sorts of food. No attacks on the scales of other fishes could be observed when kept in a community aquarium.

Breeding

Melanochromis sp. "lepidophage" is an ovophile maternal mouthbrooder, i.e. has the same reproductive biology as the other Malawi-cichlids. The mother specimen releases approximately thirty juveniles after a three week period of mouthbrooding. These readily feed on *Artemia*-nauplii.

Rocky shore of Mumbo Island in the south of Lake Malawi

The Genus Neolamprologus

COLOMBE & ALLGAYER, 1985

Neolamprologus is the largest genus of Cichlids from Lake Tanganyika after most of the species formerly accommodated in the collective genus *Lamprologus* were transferred to it. Including more recent descriptions, it presently houses approximately fifty species.

This genus is of special importance for the aquarists since the species of *Neolamprologus* are relatively small fishes whose maximum lengths exceed ten centimetres only in exceptional cases. Due to this, most of them can be kept — and even bred — in moderately large to small aquaria.

The Cichlids consolidated in this systematic unit show a surprisingly great variety of forms and ecologies. Side by side with species that may reach almost twenty centimetres *(N. tetracanthus)*, the genus also holds true dwarfs which hardly reach five centimetres *(N. kungweensis)*. Some species have remarkably elongate body shapes with almost circular cross-sections *(N. cylindricus)* whilst others are greatly compressed laterally *(N. moorii)*.

The ecologies of the members of this genus are as variable as the body shapes. Alongside with ichthyophagous predatory species, there are specialists which prey upon molluscs or small shrimps. Especially significant are the tiny ostracophil *Neolamprologus* species which utilize empty snail-shells as homes and spawning-sites. Besides rather inconspicuously coloured species there are others with bright yellow or orange colourations.

The interesting Tanganyika-cichlids are caught on the rocky shore.

◆ *Neolamprologus boulengeri*
(STEINDACHNER, 1909)

Five specimens which the couple HORN had collected in Lake Tanganyika in 1908 formed the basis for the description of this Cichlid by the ichthyologist STEINDACHNER from Vienna in 1909. Originally named *Julido-chromis boulengeri*, POLL (1946) doubted the validity of this description and assumed that the small specimens were juveniles of another species. Later (1956) he presumed that the taxon would be identic with *Neolamprologus hecqui* (BOULENGER, 1899). However, in his 1986 revision of the Cich-lids of Lake Tanganyika he revised this point of view and lists this Cichlid as a separate and valid member of the genus *Neolampro-logus*.

The same year saw the original descrip-tion of a Cichlid by MEYER and co-authors which they had deemed a new species and named *Lamprologus kirivaithai*. It did not take long until it was discovered (STAECK 1988) that this Cichlid was identic to *Neo-*

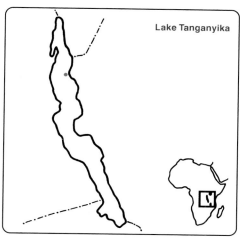

Locality of *Neolamprologus boulengeri*

lamprologus boulengeri and the new description was therefore synonymous. The first live specimens of this species appeared in German pet-shops in 1985.

Under aquarium conditions, the males of *Neolamprologus boulengeri* may reach a length of seven centimetres. Females are

Male of *Neolamprologus boulengeri*

considerably smaller and fully grown at a mere five centimetres. However, except for the difference in size, there are no other obvious sexual features which would allow an undoubted determination of the sexes.

Light brown is the predominant background-colour of *N. boulengeri* which is overlain by a blueish shine on the lateral sides of the body. The back region and mid-body are each marked with a longitudinal row of dark spots which may be arranged alternatingly, but may also be fused and thus form an irregular, partly indistinct pattern of transversal stripes on the flanks. The most distinctive colour-feature is a large black blotch in the dorsal fin that extends from the eleventh to the eighteenth spine. The pectoral fins are yellowish, the ventral fins of dominant specimens are blackish in colour. All unpairy fins are smoky grey with the anterior portion of the anal fin being orange-yellow. The dorsal fin has a broad orange-yellow margin.

The

natural habitat

of *Neolamprologus boulengeri* is the sandy littoral of Lake Tanganyika. The precise collecting locality of the type specimens is unknown. The only certain locality at the moment is in the vicinity of the town of Kigoma on the northeastern shore of the lake in Tanzania where the species was caught for the export of ornamental fishes (MEYER et al. 1986).

Care

As is the case in most of the other Tanganyika-cichlids, the successful maintenance of *Neolamprologus boulengeri* is easy if provided with moderately hard water at pHvalues in the alkaline zone. Since *Neolamprologus boulengeri* belongs to the ostracophil Cichlids, a few empty shells of the Edible Snail are required to adequately decorate the aquarium. The bottom of the tank is covered with at least five centimetres of

sand and the rear wall serves to support a construction of rocks which are arranged to form several grottos and other hiding-sites.

The social behaviour of *N. boulengeri* and the behavioural pattern centering around the empty snail shell are comparable with those observed in *N. ocellatus*. The male intends to create a shallow pit of about approximately 30 cm in diameter in the sandy ground in whose centre up to three empty snail shells may be lying. Usually the mollusc shells are positioned on the top of a small hill with the opening facing upwards. Then, they are buried in the sand until only their openings remain visible. The activity of digging is mainly taken over by the female which uses three different techniques — digging, pushing, and ploughing.

In contrast to other shell-dwelling Cichlids, the snail shells exclusively serve the females as places for sleeping and hiding, the reason being the considerable size of adult males which simply cannot fit into the snail shells. When danger lurks, they leave the territory and seek shelter in rock crevices.

Under adequate conditions, the

breeding

is not difficult. As adult females may lay more than sixty eggs at a time, the space inside a snail shell is hardly great enough to accommodate a complete clutch. One may therefore have the chance to see a part of it from outside since individual eggs are attached to the walls immediately behind the opening. The female dedicates herself to the care of the clutch whilst the male defends their joint territory. Once spawning has taken place, the aggression of the parents increases greatly. They are not even shy of the keeper's hand, but viciously attack it with bites into the upper side.

Initially, the juveniles are so perfectly camouflaged that they can hardly be spotted above the sandy ground. Although they are fairly tiny, they can easily be reared by feeding them with the nauplii of the Brine Shrimp.

◗ *Neolamprologus brevis*
(BOULENGER, 1899)

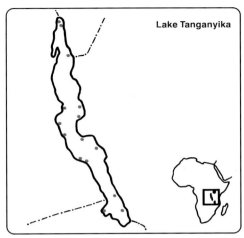

Localities of *Neolamprologus brevis*

was one of the first ostracophil Cichlids kept in aquaria with first imports being observed late in 1979. With a maximum length of just under six centimetres, this fish belongs to the Dwarf Cichlids of Lake Tanganyika. Unfortunately it is not possible to definitely distinguish the sexes by means of external feature, but mature female specimens are distinctly smaller than males.

The ground colouration of *N. brevis* is brownish beige which becomes evidently lighter towards the belly. The sides are marked with 9 narrow transversal lines which shine whitish green posteriorly and light blue in the anterior portion of the body.

Neolamprologus brevis

A conspicuous blueish lilac gleaming zone lies immediately below the eye.

The

natural habitat

of this small Cichlid is the muddy and sandy ground at places where snails of the genus *Neothauma* occur in greater numbers. The empty shells of these molluscs serve the fish as sanctuaries and spawning-caves. The fact that it is so rarely imported is explained by their preference of greater depths. There are confirmed records for this species at depths between six and much more than fifty metres. In nature, Copepods, i.e. small shrimps, appear to play a major role in the diet of this fish.

The distribution of the species seems to cover the entire lake, and localities are known from the north and the south of Zaïre, from Zambia, and all parts of Tanzania.

Care

Keeping this ostracophil Cichlid obviously requires several empty snail shells. Fortunately one does not necessarily require the original Tanganyika snails shown in the photograph. The fish also readily accept the shells of Edible Snails which have approximately the same size, but have thinner walls and a slightly deviating shape. The shells can be obtained from delicatessen shops which hold Edible Snails for fans of the French Cuisine.

The ground of the aquarium should consist of four to five centimetres of sand which enable the fish to bury their snail shells in a satisfying manner. This is usually the case when not much more than the opening sticks out of the ground. It is interesting to observe that the specimens work their house until it lies in a certain angle to the ground-surface. Only then is it ensured that they can dash into the twisted course of the snail shell in case of danger.

For these activities, the fish utilize at least three different techniques. Firstly, they directly push the house by either grasping the edge with the jaws or ramming against it. Secondly, they move it indirectly by removing sand from underneath so that it slowly rolls to one side or disappears underground. Thirdly, they might bury the shell by "ploughing" or covering it with sand. To do this, they lie on the ground and powerfully lash the tail to throw big amounts of sand backwards.

Since plants are totally ignored by this cichlid, these may be used for the decoration of the aquarium. It must however be ensured that the fish require adequately large unobstructed sandy interspaces.

It is of course possible to keep a pair of *N. brevis* in a tank of only fifty centimetres in length. But it is much more rewarding to keep several pairs in a larger aquarium and together with other Tanganyika-cichlids. It is not before this husbandry configuration is met that the highly interesting territorial and fighting behaviour can be observed to the full extent. Adequate company fishes are amongst others the Goby Cichlids, *Julidochromis transcriptus*, *J. ornatus*, and *Tropheus duboisi*.

Provided with an appropriate diet and suitable husbandry conditions, the

breeding

of *Neolamprologus brevis* does not let the keeper face specific problems. As is the case in all shell-dwelling Cichlids, the female lays her eggs inside a partly buried snail shell. The presence of a clutch can be noted from the fact that the female appears in front of the shell at regular intervals to create a current with the fins that provides the clutch inside the snail shell with fresh water. The male is not directly involved in the care for the fry, but only defends the borders of the territory. As soon as the juveniles leave the spawning-cave they must be fed with nauplii of the Brine Shrimp.

▶ *Neolamprologus brichardi*
(POLL, 1974)

is an ideal fish for the aquarium. The fish reaches a maximum length of approximately 9 cm. It is not really its colouration, but rather its elegant body shape and fins that make it such an attractive species. Since males and females look the same, a determination of the sexes by means of external features is impossible. The ground colouration of the body is brownish beige. The upper angle of the operculum is marked with an orange spot, and the cheeks have a pattern of turquoise speckles. Specific traits are the pitch black streak that connects the eye with the operculum and the same coloured margin of the gill-cover.

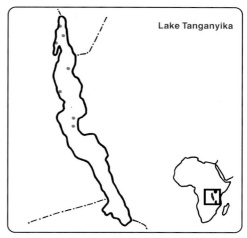

Lake Tanganyika

Localities of *Neolamprologus brichardi*

Neolamprologus brichardi

93

The

natural habitat

of this Cichlid is the lower portion of the rubble- and rocky littoral. Its distribution appears to be confined to the northern half of Lake Tanganyika.

The fish seem to be especially frequent at depths between five and ten metres. They are never encountered alone or in pairs, but always in larger groups which inhabit a certain area. They feed on small items such as small shrimps and other invertebrates which are collected from the lawn of algae.

The

care

in a naturally decorated aquarium is no problem. If the fish is kept amongst its own kind, a small aquarium of fifty to ninety centimetres in length is sufficient. If they are housed in a community tank, they claim a lot more space for their territory in which they rear their offspring and which they are determined to defend. Despite their moderate size they manage to enforce their will even against much larger Cichlids. Adequate company fishes of the community aquarium are species of the genera *Tropheus, Julidochromis, Telmatochromis, Chalinochromis,* and the smaller representatives of *Neolamprologus.* The decoration of the aquarium calls for rocks and stones. These are piled up on the rear wall so that many crevices and hiding-places are created. The rock construction should reach up to just under the water surface. Since *N. brichardi* leaves even most fragile plants alone, planting the aquarium is possible. It should be ensured that enough swimming-space remains. Except for the lawn of algae there are no plants in the natural biotope.

The

breeding

may take place in the community tank if it is not intended to rear large numbers of juveniles. This species' intensive care for the fry ensures that a part of the offspring survives even under these conditions. *N. brichardi* is a cave brooder which hides its spawn in narrow rock-crevices. The parental care behaviour of this species is unusual because the juveniles grow up in a clan-family. Older siblings participate in the task of caring for the young and assist the parents with their rearing. Even after they have reached maturity they are tolerated in the territory so that they eventually form a clan. This is the explanation why the species is always encountered in large groups in nature. The juveniles are very tiny and require nauplii of *Artemia salina* or MikroMin as first food. They need not be fed separately in a large community aquarium since sufficient amounts of small and very small food particles are always left over by the other, bigger fishes.

Rubble-zone in the Sumbu National Park (Zambia)

◗ *Neolamprologus callipterus*
(BOULENGER, 1906)

This ostracophil Cichlid of Lake Tanganyika was originally described on the basis of four specimens of which the largest measured 12,5 cm. In the same publication, BOU-LENGER introduced another Cichlid under the name of *Lamprologus reticulatus* which had a length of only 6,5 cm. In 1946, POLL eventually found out that the large and the small fishes were actually the same species, and *L. reticulatus* would, due to priority reasons, be a junior synonym.

The Belgian Hydrobiological Expedition of 1946/47 eventually caught more than 250 specimens of this Cichlid. A surprising result of the examination of this collection was that although a maximum length of 15,4 centimetres can be reached, a high percentage of the caught specimens measured only

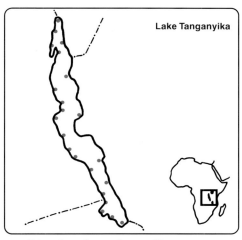

Localities of *Neolamprologus callipterus*

between four and four and a half centimetres (POLL 1956). The explanation for this curious circumstance was only found 30

Male of *Neolamprologus callipterus*

years later when the fish was studied in its natural habitat and in the aquarium (STAECK 1987). In *Neolamprologus callipterus,* there is a highly unusual difference in the adult size of males and females with males reaching three times the length of females. The latter are fully grown at a length of four to five centimetres.

The

natural habitat

of *Neolamprologus callipterus* lies in the lower shore-zone of Lake Tanganyika at depths between five and seventy metres (POLL 1956). Own observations showed that the fish inhabits the transitory zone from rocky to sandy ground. Here, adult males claim breeding territories which they mark by compiling empty shells of snails of the genus *Neothauma* from even far off. One-hundred to twohundred of these snail shells are usually placed in a shallow pit of approximately one metre in diameter. Each breeding territory is home to several females. Observations in the aquarium showed that fully grown males are capable

to carry snail shells around with a female specimen inside (KASSELMANN 1987). They do not become territorial before they have grown to a size which enables them to carry snailshells over wider distances in order to establish a breeding territory. In contrast, younger males of six to ten centimetres consolidate to larger schools and together roam the shore-zone in search of food.

The

care

requires just a number of empty shells of the Edible Snail, a few stone-plates which are arranged to form cave-like hiding-places, and a bottom of at least five centimetres of sand.

Breeding

The males attempt to consolidate several females in their territories with whom they alternatingly spawn. The females care for the fry alone. The juveniles are fairly tiny when they leave the snail shell and show little bonding to the spawning-territory.

Female of *Neolamprologus callipterus*

◆ *Neolamprologus fasciatus*
(BOULENGER, 1898)

belongs to the Tanganyika-cichlids hardly known amongst aquarists, the major reason certainly being this fish is rarely imported. Their maximum length is around fourteen centimetres. Distinguishing the sexes by means of external features is impossible. Both sexes have an ochre to ivory background colouration and a pattern of approximately nine, partly forked dark transversal bands. A typical trait of this species is the turquoise colour of the iris.

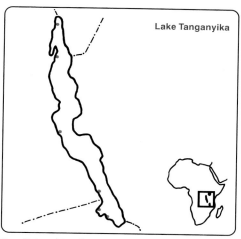

Localities of *Neolamprologus fasciatus*

The

natural habitat

is the rubble- and rocky littoral. In Zambia, I could observe this fish at depths of two to five metres. Further localities are known from the west and the northwest coast in Zaïre.

The fish preferably find their food amongst the lawn of algae that covers stones and rocks. Small fresh-water shrimps apparently play an important role in their diet.

Care

Carning for this species is not difficult. Keeping it is most promising in a community aquarium of more than one metre in

Neolamprologus fasciatus

length. Adequate company fishes are other small to not too large species of *Neolamprologus* as well as Cichlids of the genera *Julidochromis, Chalinochromis, Telmatochromis, Spathodus,* and *Eretmodus* which also inhabit the upper regions of the shore-zone with its rocky ground. Basically, it appears to be also possible to keep it together with species of *Tropheus*. If too many of these restless and eagerly feeding fishes are around, there is the risk that the timid *N. fasciatus* do not feel at ease and have problems to obtain their share of the food. It is insufficient to feed adult specimens on an exclusive diet of *Daphnia* and flake-food. This need to be supplemented by more potent types of prey such as White Mosquito larvae, *Mysis*-shrimps, or the grated meat of Deep-sea Shrimps.

The aquarium should be decorated with rocks piled up against the rear wall so that dens are created and the division of the available space into territories is simplified. Although the natural biotope is bare of plants, these may be used to a certain extend since *N. fasciatus* ignores them.

Very little information is available on the

breeding,

the main reason certainly being the fact that this Cichlid is so rarely imported and if so, usually comes in single specimens. Provided that the fish is kept in a naturally decorated aquarium, it should not be particularly difficult to get a pair to breed. An important precondition for successful breeding will unquestionably be the right feeding. Promising attempts may take place by keeping a pair in an aquarium of about one metre in length or in a spacious community tank where it is housed together with other species of *Neolamprologus*.

Neolamprologus fasciatus and *Neolamprologus moorii* at two metres depth in the rubble-zone

◗ *Neolamprologus furcifer*
(BOULENGER, 1898)

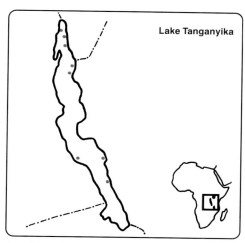

Lake Tanganyika

Localities of *Neolamprologus furcifer*

is a highly interesting fish for the aquarium and belongs to the most noteworthy Cichlids of Lake Tanganyika. The maximum body length of this species is close to 15 centimetres. It is more or less monomorphous, which means male and female specimens have almost no distinctive external features. Older males can however be recognized by having a fat-bulge on the occiput.

The ground colouration is highly variable and may be copper-red, ochre, or greyish beige. The flanks of the body may be marked with six, dark, transversal bands. Their presence or absence depends on the prevailing mood. A conspicuous trait of this species is the golden yellow and azure-blue shining iris. Another specific feature is the deeply forked caudal fin which ends in two long points in older specimens.

The natural habitat

of this fish is the upper rubble- and rocky littoral. Its distribution seems to extend over the entire lake. Localities are known from the western and northwestern shore (Zaïre), the northeastern shore (Burundi, Tanzania), and the central east coast (Tanzania). No other species of *Neolamprologus* is known which is so firmly bonded to the presence of caves and crevices. During the day, these fish are hardly ever seen outside their dens.

Neolamprologus furcifer

Their behaviour has many parallels to that of the species of *Julidochromis* which are comparatively firmly bonded to rocky substrates. For example, *N. furcifer* also likes to stay on the ceiling of a cave by swimming upside down. The natural diet is poorly researched. Examinations of stomach-contents indicated that insect larvae were preyed upon.

Care

Keeping this fish rather takes place in a community aquarium of one and a half metres in length. Appropriate company fishes are primarily the smaller species of *Julidochromis* and *Neolamprologus*. On the other hand, *Tropheus moorii* is less adequate since this fish is too restless. As observation in the natural habitat showed, *N. furcifer* requires grottos to feel at ease to an even greater extend than the case is in other Tanganyika-cichlids from the rubble- and rocky littoral. Remember this peculiarity when it comes to the decoration of the aquarium.

Unfortunately, this species has a high degree of intraspecific aggression, and only the breeding partner is tolerated in the territory. However, in a community tank, the presence of other fishes considerably reduces the natural aggression towards specimens of their own kind.

Since *N. furcifer* does not damage plants, the aquarium may be planted to a certain extend. But one should bear in mind that the natural biotope of this Cichlid is devoid of plants. After a period of adjustment which may sometimes take up to half a year, the fish readily feeds, besides *Daphnia* and mosquito larvae, also on flakefood such as TetraMin and TetraCichlid. Larger specimens should additionally be offered larger prey-items, e.g. adequately sized meat of fish and shrimps.

For the purpose of

breeding

the fish should be kept in pairs in a naturally decorated aquarium of approximately one metre in length. It is an adapted cave brooder which preferably spawns on the ceiling of its spawning-cave. The eggs, larvae, and juveniles are cared for in a parental family-structure. The hatchlings are small and must therefore be reared on a diet of nauplii of *Artemia salina* and powdered flake-food. To date, the breeding of *N. furcifer* was successful only in a few isolated cases. The main reason for this is the rarity of imports.

Kasaba Bay in Zambia

◆ *Neolamprologus lemairii*
(BOULENGER, 1899)

belongs to the larger representatives of the genus. The fish may reach up to 24 centimetres and a weight of 150 gram. Due to this reason they are rarely imported and are thus fairly unknown to the aquaristic hobby. Since males and females have an identical appearance, the identification of the sexes by means of external traits is impossible.

The upper half of the body is yellowish to olive-grey whilst the lower one is beige to greyish beige. The sides are marked with three to four, broad, dark, transversally arranged bands. A typical feature of this species is the big size of the eyes and the deeply grooved large mouth. In comparison with other representatives of the genus *N. lemairii* has a remarkably stout and plump body shape. In contrast to adults, juveniles have a relatively slender and elongate body shape up to a length of about two centimetres. Their colour pattern is also different from the more camouflage-like colouration of the adults. They have an ochre ground colouration with a pattern of several greatly contrasting black bands which obliquely run from the belly to the back region. A few light shining scales are irregularly scattered over the flanks. The pectoral, dorsal, and anal fins are deep yellow in colour and

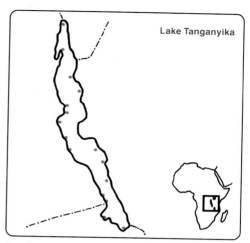

Localities of *Neolamprologus lemairii*

bordered with black. The inner area of the ventral fins and the base of the dorsal fin are black whereas the outer regions are ochre.

The

natural habitats

lie in the shore-zone of Lake Tanganyika. Although the fish has been recorded from depths below thirty metres, it is more common at shallow levels. In contrast to other species of *Neolamprologus*, the distribution

Neolamprologus lemairii

of this Cichlid is not restricted to a certain type of biotope. Thus, it has not only been recorded from the rubble and rocky littoral, but has also often been found above sandy or muddy ground. This ecological flexibility is obviously the reason for the records of this species from all parts of the lake. *N. lemairi* is a predatory fish which, from a certain size on, exclusively feeds on other fishes, usually other Cichlids. The prey is not caught in pursuit, but in ambush.

Care

According to experiences keeping *Neolamprologus lemairii* lets the aquarist face certain problems. Being specialized on large prey-items and able to swallow fishes of surprisingly big size, adult specimens can only be kept together with other large Cichlids such as *Neolamprologus tetracanthus* or *Lepidiolamprologus elongatus*.

On the other hand, this ambuscader has a fairly calm temperament and may be kept in comparatively small aquaria. The decoration is of minor importance, but a few rocks and groups of plants should provide covered spots.

According to the feeding ecology in nature, larger specimens need to be regularly fed with pieces of fish.

The captive

breeding

has apparently not yet been successful. Observations in the natural environment revealed that also this species of *Neolamprologus* is a cave brooder. The fry is reared in a father-mother-family in which the female seems to be more dedicated to the direct care whilst the male defends the territory.

Transitory zone from the sandy to the rocky zone (central eastern coast of Lake Tanganyika near Karongwe)

◗ *Neolamprologus longior*
(STAECK, 1980)

This bright coloured Cichlid was originally described as a subspecies of *Neolamprologus leleupi* (POLL, 1956). Although both forms resemble each other closely, POLL (1986) granted both of them separate species status. Since either of them have not only bright yellow colourations, but also resembling body shapes, they can easily be mistaken. However, *Neolamprologus leleupi* is more lemon-yellow and *N. longior* more deep yellow. The colouration of this Cichlid depends not only on the husbandry conditions, but also on the diet. A more reliable trait of distinction than the colour is therefore the shape of the body. *Neolamprologus*

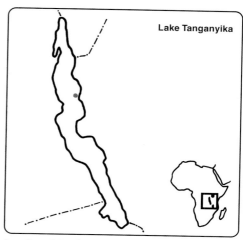

Locality of *Neolamprologus longior*

Neolamprologus longior

longior is conspicuously slender and elongate whereas *N. leleupi* is more stout and high-backed.

Neolamprologus longior ranks amongst the best known and most popular fishes of Lake Tanganyika, the reason being not only its attractive colouration, but also its small size. Growing up to ten centimetres, the fish is monomorphous, i.e. males and females look more or less the same and almost indistinguishable. It appears that fully grown females are slightly smaller.

In contrast to *Neolamprologus leleupi* whose localities lie in the northwestern corner of Lake Tanganyika in Zaïre, the

natural habitat

of *Neolamprologus longior* is situated on the eastern shore in Tanzania. The distribution of this species appears to be restricted to a short section of the coast between Kabogo Point and Kibwe Bay.

The fish is an inhabitant of the lower rocky littoral and is more frequently found below depths of five metres. The top level of its range is approximately two metres. In contrast to other species of *Neolamprologus*, this Cichlid lives in solitude outside the reproduction seasons. It is to be presumed that major prey is *Daphnia* and small freshwater shrimps.

Care

The can be problems with keeping *Neolamprologus leleupi*. The successful maintenance of this Cichlid requires a well harmonizing pair and an aquarium at least half a metre long. A natural decoration will take rocks and stone-plates into consideration which are arranged in such a manner that numerous crevices and grottos are created. Light sand or fine gravel should be chosen as substrate. There are indications that the fish adapts to the colour of the ground, and with a very dark substrate present, they assume a more brownish tone than the bright yellow colouration.

Neolamprologus longior does not damage plants, but it should be borne in mind that there is no vegetation in its natural biotope. When planting the aquarium it should be ensured that sufficient unobstructed swimming-space is left.

Feeding this Cichlid is a problem in so far that an inappropriate diet eventually leads to a change in the colouration from bright yellow to a dirty brownish yellow. Offering food containing carotin is therefore a must and small shrimps, preferably *Cyclops*, and *Daphnia* of the genera *Daphnia* and *Bosmina* should regularly be given. TetraRubin, a flake-food supplemented with colourpigment, also helps to retain the splendid colours of this fish.

It is of course possible to keep *Neolamprologus longior* in a community aquarium. Adequate company fishes can be found amongst other inhabitants of the rocky littoral, e.g. species of *Julidochromis*, *Chalinochromis*, *Telmatochromis*, small *Neolamprologus*, and Goby Cichlids. Although a socialization with *Tropheus duboisi* or *T. moorii* is possible, it cannot be recommended since these fishes are too restless.

For the

breeding

the fish should not be separately kept in pairs, but left in the community aquarium in the company of other small Cichlids from the rocky littoral. The tank needs to be decorated according to nature, i.e. contain a number of caves and alcoves which can be used as hiding-places. In too small aquaria, the males may become very aggressive towards the females.

Neolamprologus longior is a cave brooder. The fry is reared in a father-mother-family, which means that both parental specimens take over separate tasks. Since the juveniles are initially very small, only newly hatched nauplii of *Artemia salina* and finely crushed flake-food are appropriate.

◆ *Neolamprologus modestus*
(BOULENGER, 1898)

Southern colour morph

This Cichlid reaches a maximum length of approximately twelve centimetres. The fish is slate-grey to blueish grey in colour with the sexes being difficult to determine since males and females do not differ in external traits. Male specimens however grow larger and have slightly more pointed dorsal and anal fins.

The species is commonly found everywhere in Lake Tanganyika. Its preferred

natural habitat

is the upper rubble- and rocky littoral. The specimen shown in the photograph was caught in the Nkamba Bay (Zambia). Its origin can be determined by the colour of the pectoral fins; only specimens from the southern portion of Lake Tanganyika have the conspicuously yellow coloured pectorals

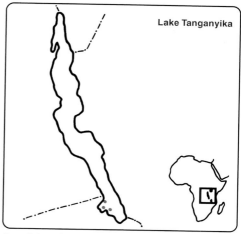

Localities of the southern colour morph of *Neolamprologus modestus*

whilst the fins are colourless in the northern half of the lake.

Snails and mussels apparently play an important role in the diet of *Neolamprologus modestus*.

Neolamprologus modestus, southern colour morph

The

care

should preferably be tried in a community aquarium one to one and a half metres long. In accordance with the conditions in the natural biotope, it should offer numerous caves and alcoves which result from piling up rocks and stone-plates. They provide the fish with the necessary hiding-sites and enable them to define several territories.

The decoration may also include plants as *N. modestus* does not feed on, or damage them. The fish only begins to dig in the ground when there is no adequate cover available.

Suitable company fishes are other Tanganyika-cichlids from the rubble- or rocky zones, e.g. species of *Julidochromis*, *Telmatochromis*, *Cyprichromis*, or *Neolamprologus*.

Feeding this species is no problem as all common types of food are accepted. Adult specimens should not be kept on an exclusive diet of *Daphnia* and flake-food, but regularly be fed with insect larvae and appropriately grated meat of fish and shrimps (deep-sea shrimps).

The

breeding

requires an aquarium of fifty to ninety centimetres in length in which a pair is housed separately. Although the fish also easily breeds in the community tank, only a few juveniles will grow up whilst the majority becomes prey for the company fishes. The young *Neolamprologus modestus* do not lead the furtive life of juvenile *Julidochromis*, but form a school which rises from the ground and stays in the centre of the territory defended by the parents.

Like the majority of the representatives of this genus, *N. modestus* is a cave brooder. The care for and protection of the fry is equally shared by both parents. The juveniles are relatively small and initially require freshly hatched nauplii of the Brine Shrimp, *Artemia salina*, and finely crushed flake-food or MikroMin.

Vegetation zone of Lake Tanganyika in two metres depth

◆ *Neolamprologus moorii*
(BOULENGER, 1898)

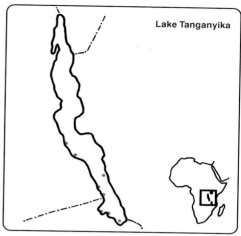

Localities of *Neolamprologus moorii*

belongs to the smaller representatives of its genus and reaches a maximum length of a little more than ten centimetres. This species is a noteworthy exception in the genus *Neolamprologus* in so far that it has a fairly distinct age-dependant multichromatism. The layman would therefore probably not assign juvenile and adult specimens to the same species.

Adult *N. moorii* are uniformly slate-grey, with only the margins of the unpairy fins being pretty azure-blue. In contrast, juveniles are uniformly golden to honey-yellow. With age, the yellow becomes darker, and on reaching a length of five centimetres the fish has turned brownish. Subsequently, this tone eventually changes to grey.

Neolamprologus moori is monomorphous, i.e. there are no obvious differences between males and females, thus making it extremely difficult to identify the sexes of specimens. Usable hints may be found in the shapes of the fins when the fish are adult. Fully grown males generally have distinctly

Juvenile of *Neolamprologus moorii*

longer ventral fins than females. Their dorsal and anal fins are also more produced.

The

natural habitat

of this species is the rubble- and rocky zone near the shore. Here, it is regularly found together with *Tropheus moorii*, *Neolamprologus modestus*, *N. mustax*, *Chalinochromis brichardi*, *Julidochromis regani*, and *Eretmodus cyanostictus*. I have never managed to find this Cichlid below a depth of three metres. The major source of food obviously lies in the lawn of algae. Examinations of stomach contents by POLL showed that, besides crustaceans and other micro-organisms, filamentous algae were also fed upon. The distribution of this Cichlid appears to be restricted to the southern part of the lake. All locality records were made in Zambia, southern Zaïre, and Tanzania respectively.

The

care

in a community aquarium of approximately one and a half metres in length and together with other Tanganyika-cichlids from the upper rubble- or rocky littoral promises very interesting observations. Such an aquarium should emulate the conditions of the natural biotope as closely as possible. Rocks and stones are piled up along the rear wall in such a manner that crevices and alcoves of different sizes are created. Appropriate plants are primarily those which anchor themselves on the rock-constructions (*Microsorum pteropus*, *Anubias* sp.). This ensures that the foreground remains unobstructed and can thus serve as swimming-space for the fishes. A densely planted aquarium would be inadequate as there is no such vegetation in the rocky littoral of Lake Tanganyika.

After a short period of adjustment, *Neolamprologus moorii* accepts all common

Fully coloured adult specimen of *Neolamprologus moorii*

types of food. If *Daphnia,* White Mosquito larvae, and TetraPhyll are offered alternatingly, a sufficient and varying diet is ensured.

For

breeding

it is not essential to transfer a pair to a separate aquarium. In a naturally decorated tank with no overpopulation a few juveniles will always grow up without problems. As most of the species of *Neolamprologus, N. moorii* is a cave brooder. A relatively firm bonding develops between the reproduction partners. They care for and defend their fry together. At a temperature of 26 °C, the juveniles leave the spawning-cave approxi-

mately one week after spawning. Forming a dense school, they then swim a few centimetres above the ground. I could observe the same situation in the natural habitat on numerous occasions.

In comparison with West African cave brooders, the behaviour of the juvenile *N. moorii* is different in the fact that they do not explore their environment under the guidance of their parents. The group of young *Neolamprologus* is rather confined to a specific location in the immediate vicinity of the spawning-cave which is defended by both parents.

Although the juveniles are fairly small, they are easily reared on a diet of nauplii of the Brine Shrimp and finely powdered flake-food.

Locality of *Neolamprologus moorii*

◗ *Neolamprologus savoryi*
(POLL, 1949)

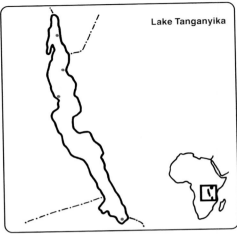

Lake Tanganyika

is one of the smaller representatives of this genus with the maximum body length being just under nine centimetres. This fish is not particularly bright in its colours. The background colouration of the body is silvery grey, becoming darker towards the back and lighter towards the belly. As in *Neolamprologus brichardi,* the operculum has a pitch black hind edge. Six dark transversal bands mark the flanks between the edge of the operculum and the base of the tail. The fish is monomorphous, i.e. males and females do not differ in their appearances. It is therefore impossible to distinguish between the sexes on the basis of external features.

Localities of *Neolamprologus savoryi*

The *natural habitat*

is the rubble-zone near the shore. As far as suitable biotopes are available the fish appears to occur everywhere in Lake Tanganyika. Localities have been recorded from the northern shore (Burundi, Tanzania), the central west coast (Zaïre), and from the

Neolamprologus savoryi

southern tip of the lake (Zambia). Neverthe-less they are difficult to observe and to catch as they lead a fairly furtive life, residing more between the stones than above them. They do not appear to be highly specialized feeders, and sustain on the lawn of algae. Examinations of stomach contents by POLL showed that specimens had eaten insect lar-vae, small shrimps, and plant-material.

The

care

is not difficult and for a pair, an aquarium of half a metre in length may be sufficient. Observations made in the natural biotopes suggest that they require hiding-sites and grottos to feel at ease. The decoration of the tank should therefore primarily consist of rocks and stone-plates which are arranged accordingly.

As is the case in other species of *Neolam-prologus,* this Cichlid is also plant-tolerant. Planting the aquarium is therefore possible, but should be limited and leave enough unobstructed swimming-space. Except for algae the natural biotopes are free of vegeta-tion.

With its deeply grooved mouth *N. savo-ryi* is an omnivore and capable of swallow-ing fairly large food-items. It is thus easy to feed. The diet should nevertheless be vary-ing and, besides *Daphnia* and insect larvae, include flake-food such as TetraMin, TetraPhyll, TetraCichlid, and TetraCichlid Sticks.

In a community aquarium, the fish gets along well with other Tanganyika-cichlids from the rubble-littoral. In this case the tank should at least measure one and a half metres in length since *Neolamprologus savo-ryi* claims a fairly large territory. As soon as there are juveniles around, this is vehe-mently defended even against larger Cich-lids. Adequate company fishes may be the larger species of *Julidochromis, Telmato-chromis,* and *Neolamprologus.*

Reports on the successful

breeding

of this species are rare. However, the reason is not that this Cichlid is difficult to breed, but that it is so rarely imported. The species usually only arrives at the importers in single specimens which have incidentally slipped into a shipment. To assemble a breeding pair is therefore very difficult.

Neolamprologus savoryi is a cave brooder. Male and female jointly care for and protect their fry. The juveniles are fairly small and initially hide away carefully. Like juvenile *Julidochromis* they hardly ever come off the substrate and are thus difficult to spot. They are reared on a diet of freshly hatched nau-plii of the Brine Shrimp *Artemia salina* and MikroMin or finely powdered flake-food.

Nets and plastic bins with holes have been mounted to these tubes and serve as short-term storing con-tainers for freshly caught Tanganyika-cichlids.

◗ *Neolamprologus sexfasciatus*
(TREWAVAS & POLL, 1952)

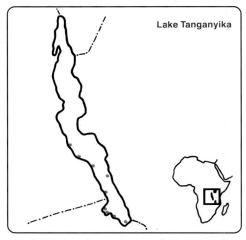

Localities of *Neolamprologus sexfasciatus*

undoubtedly ranks amongst the most conspicuous Cichlids from Lake Tanganyika. On a greyish white to silvery ground, the fish has six, pitch black, transversal bands. The first of which crosses over the operculum and the posteriormost one lies on the base of the tail. A very similar, and in fact closely allied species, is *Neolamprologus tretocephalus*. The major point of distinction between these two species and the one which allows a reliable identification is that *N. tretocephalus* has one band less, i.e. only five, on the flanks.

  N. sexfasciatus belongs to the monomorphous Cichlids. With males not differing from females in external characteristics, it is obviously difficult to determine the sex of a specimen. However, in pairs which I observed in the natural habitat, the male was always larger than the female. The maximum body length of this species may be approximately 15 centimetres.

The *natural habitat*

is the rubble- and rocky zone near the shore. Here, the fish mainly reside in depths between two and three metres and appear to not occur below five metres. It is frequently observed in pairs, sometimes with juveniles whom they care for. Molluscs like small snails appear to play an important role in their diet.

  It appears that the distribution of this species is confined to the southern half of Lake Tanganyika with all known localities

Neolamprologus sexfasciatus

either lying on the west coast (Zaïre), in the south (Zambia), or on the southeastern shore (Tanzania). In the vicinity of Kipli on the southeastern coast, a population has been discovered in which the greyish white ground colouration is replaced by lemon-yellow. Whether this is just a new colour morph or a subspecies still needs to be investigated in detail.

Care

Keeping *Neolamprologus sexfasciatus* presents no problems. For this moderately large Cichlid a large community aquarium with a minimum length of one and a half metres appears to be best suitable. Company fishes should comprise of other Tanganyika-cichlids from the upper rubble- and rocky littoral. Representatives of the genera *Julidochromis, Telmatochromis, Spathodus,* and other *Neolamprologus* appear to be very appropriate. The socialization with a small group of *Tropheus* is possible though not ideal since these Cichlids are too active and restless. By means of a respective decoration it should be tried to emulate the natural conditions as closely as possible. Therefore, numerous pieces of rock are needed which are piled up preferably against the back wall in an arrangement that creates hiding-caves of different shapes and sizes.

Although there are no plants but algae in the natural biotope of these Cichlids, planting the tank to a certain extend is possible as the fish even ignore delicate shoots. It is recommendable to focus primarily on those species which anchor on the rock-constructions and do not require the substrate of the ground. This includes, amongst others, *Anubias nana* and *Microsorum pteropus.*

Feeding *Neolamprologus sexfasciatus* is no problem. After a certain period of adjustment all common types of food are accepted including flake-food. Adult specimens will only eat if meat of fish, *Mysis*-shrimps, or grated Deep-sea Shrimps are offered.

The
breeding

was successful only in a few isolated cases. The major reason for failing attempts to breed this species in captivity previously was most likely an inadequate diet. *Neolamprologus sexfasicatus* is usually kept together with species of *Tropheus* which are extraordinarily eager feeders. The slower *Neolamprologus* thus generally acquire an insufficient share under these keeping conditions. This is added by the fact that the types of food that keep the *Tropheus* in optimal shape are inadequate for the *Neolamprologus.*

Like the majority of species of *Neolamprologus*, this Cichlid is also a cave brooder. Eggs, larvae, and juveniles are cared for and protected by both parents. Once the larval development is finalized, the fry appears like a cloud in front of the spawning-cave. In contrast to West African cave brooders they do not form a school which is guided by the parents. Instead, the young *Neolamprologus sexfasciatus* stay in the vehemently defended territory of the parents until they reach a length of about two centimetres.

Since the juveniles are initially fairly small, their rearing requires freshly hatched nauplii of the Brine Shrimp *(Artemia salina)* and MikroMin or finely powdered flake-food.

Neolamprologus tretocephalus can easily be mistaken for *N. sexfasciatus.*

◗ *Neolamprologus signatus*
(POLL, 1952)

Although this Cichlid was still assigned to the genus *Lamprologus* in the latest revision of the Tanganyika-cichlids (POLL 1968), it appears to be more adequate to allocate it to the genus *Neolamprologus*.

Live specimens were imported into Europe for the first time in the late eighties. *Neolamprologus signatus* is a shell-dwelling Cichlid which however differs from other members of this ecological group by several behavioural attributes.

It is unusual that adult specimens of this species have a very distinct sexual dichromatism. Adult males are laterally marked with a pattern of twelve or thirteen dark transversal bands, and their unpairy fins also show a striped pattern. The latter are colourless and translucent in the females, who

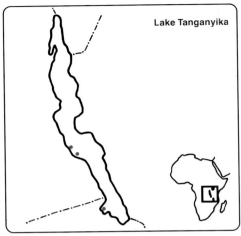

Lake Tanganyika

Localities of *Neolamprologus signatus*

also lack transversal bands on the flanks. On the other hand, the belly region of females has a conspicuous golden to greenish violet,

Female of *Neolamprologus signatus*

metallic shine from which the dark margins of the scales stand out as a reticulated pattern. The colourful belly of the female plays an important role in the social behaviour of the fish and is presented to the males as a peace-making signal during courtship as well as in quarrels.

Neolamprologus signatus ranks amongst the smallest Cichlid from Lake Tanganyika with the males hardly exceeding five centimetres in length. Females are even fully grown at a mere four centimetres.

The

natural habitat

of *Neolamprologus signatus* lies in the lower shore-zone of Lake Tanganyika in areas with sandy and muddy ground. The fish has been recorded from depths greater than fifty metres. Professional catchers of ornamental fish reported that they caught *N. signatus* in Zambia in the vicinity of Cape Nundo and Cape Kabwe Ngosye between Sumbu Bay and Nkamba Bay respectively. Here, the fish allegedly not only inhabit empty snail shells, but also caves excavated from the ground of the lake. Further locality records were made in the vicinity of the villages of Moba and M'toto on the west coast.

Care

Keeping this small Cichlid requires little more than a few empty shells of the Edible Snail and fine sand which should cover the bottom of the aquarium with a layer of at least five centimetres. Unlike other shell-dwelling Cichlids the male and female do not inhabit one snail shell each, but constantly commute between several shells which they use simultaneously.

Breeding

A special trait of this species is the fact that their eggs have lost the ability to stick to the spawning substrate. They obviously lie loosely inside the snail shell and are — like the larvae transported from one shell to another several times. It is furthermore unusual that the male participates in the process of relocating the fry.

Male of *Neolamprologus signatus*

◗ *Neolamprologus* sp.
"cygnus"

This scientifically undescribed Cichlid which most likely is a species of *Neolamprologus* was first imported into Europe in 1988.

It is a fish with a deeply forked caudal fin and therefore has an appearance similar to *Neolamprologus christyi* and the species of the *Neolamprologus brichardi*-complex. Its comparatively pointed head, the elongate body, and the dark colour pattern of adult specimens more resembles *N. christyi* whereas the size of fully grown specimens — they reach only just under ten centimetres in total length — more corresponds with *N. brichardi*.

The special feature of this Cichlid is a drastic age-depending change of colour. As in the case of *N. moorii*, it has a very con-

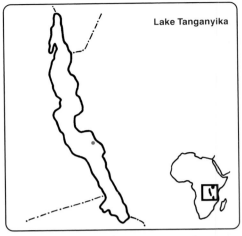

Locality of *Neolamprologus* sp. "cygnus"

spicuous juvenile colouration which is in great contrast with the more unobtrusive appearance of adult specimens. The young

Juvenile specimen of *Neolamprologus* sp. "cygnus"

fishes reach the peak of their beauty at a length of two to three centimetres. The ventral fins as well as the outer sections of the dorsal and anal fins are bright light blue whereas the bases of these fins are deep orange in colour. Except for the light blue coloured hind margin, the caudal fin is uniformly orange-yellow. The region of the head also has such orange-yellow colour-zones which are in great contrast to the brownish to slightly blueish body colouration. Unfortunately this splendid juvenile pattern fades with age. On reaching a length of approximately five centimetres, it has usually vanished and the adult fish show a drab brown to ochre colouration. The only distinct colour feature remaining is the bright light blue colour of the eyes. The unpairy fins have a speckled pattern and narrow dark margins each bordered with light submarginal lines.

The

natural habitat

of this Cichlid is the rocky littoral of Lake Tanganyika. The only known locality lies on the eastern shore in the vicinity of the village of Ikola in Tanzania (KONINGS 1991).

Care

Keeping this fish has turned out to be very easy. It is recommendable to pay attention to a varying diet and medium-hard water with an alkaline quality and as little contamination as possible. The fish may also be kept in a relatively small aquarium if one has a harmonizing pair available. Being an inhabitant of the rocky zone, this species requires rock-constructions that offer sanctuaries and spawning-caves in sufficient numbers to feel at ease.

The

breeding

The fish belongs to the territorial cave brooders and rear their fry in a parental family without distinct task-sharing. It is a species with a relatively furtive behaviour and, like *N. savoryi*, often produces only very small clutches of some ten eggs. However, it spawns frequently and in short intervals.

Fully coloured adult specimen of *Neolamprologus* sp. "cygnus"

117

The Genus Nimbochromis

ECCLES & TREWAVAS, 1989

This genus incorporates seven species which all have a predatory feeding habit and a colour pattern of large dark cloudy blotches that often merge. Although they grow to a fairly large size they are very popular amongst aquarists.

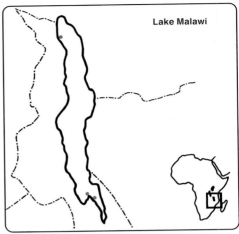

Lake Malawi

▶ *Nimbochromis polystigma*

(REGAN, 1921)

belongs to the larger representatives of the genus and may reach a length of some 23 centimetres, but usually remains smaller under aquarium conditions. Maturity is gained at approximately twelve centimetres. Like most *Nimbochromis* this species also has a distinct sexual dichromatism with females having a pattern of small reddish brown dots arranged in irregular longitudinal stripes on a beige to light grey ground colouration. Juveniles already show this pat-

Localities of *Nimbochromis polystigma*

tern when they leave the mouth of the mother. On reaching maturity, the males loose these distinct markings. The lower part of the head then becomes metallic yellowish green and the nape and area behind the eyes assume an azure-blue colouration. The rest of the body is more or less uniformly greenish.

Fully coloured male of *Nimbochromis polystigma*

The
natural habitats
are exclusive to areas near the shores of Lake Malawi. The fish is wide-ranging and relatively common in the southern portion of the lake. Unlike most of the other Malawi-cichlids, it does not show preference for a specific ground, and I could observe it in the rocky zone, above sandy ground, and in vegetated areas.

From a certain size on, *N. polystigma* appears to primarily be an ichthyophagous predatory fish preferably catching its prey from ambush. Its colour pattern serves as a perfect camouflage and thus is an adaption to this type of ecology.

According to its adult size, the fish requires much space so that its

care
calls for a spacious aquarium of considerably more than one metre in length. To make the specimen feel at ease, a number sanctuaries are required amongst the piled up rocks. As this species can be regarded plant-tolerant, the tank may be greened with hardy larger plants.

This is another mouthbrooder where a male should be kept together with two or, even better, three females. The fish should not be kept on its own, but in a community aquarium where the presence of other fishes reduces the intraspecific aggression. *N. polystigma* is a robust species and does well in the company of other large Haplochromines such as Mbuna-cichlids of the genera *Melanochromis, Pseudotropheus,* and *Labeotropheus.*

On having reached a length of approximately ten centimetres the rapidly growing fish is capable of swallowing surprisingly large prey and cannot be sufficiently sustained with *Daphnia* any more. Its diet must therefore include fish-meat and shrimps (deep-sea shrimps etc.) as well as TetraCichlid Sticks. Being meat of a warm-blooded animal, ox-heart is no optimal food and

should therefore only be given in exceptional cases.

Provided with sufficient space the

breeding
is no problem. It should take place in the community aquarium from which the mouth-breeding female is removed shortly before the larval development is completed. The spawning site is determined by the male. In most of the cases it is a horizontal stone-plate in the centre of his territory. The spawning act corresponds to the pattern typical for most of the Haplochromines.

N. polystigma is very productive with a larger female laying up to one hundred eggs at a time. Containing high amounts of yolk, the development up to the juvenile fish takes long if compared with substratum-spawners. At a water-temperature of 26 °C, the young fish are spat out by the female after almost three weeks. When eventually leaving the mouth of the mother, they are relatively large and fairly independent. In situations of danger or during the night, they return into the mouth of the mother. This care for the offspring may last for another fortnight.

Due to its size the fry can initially be fed with selected small *Daphnia* and crushed flake-food.

Larva of *Nimbochromis polystigma* on the 16th day after fertilization of the egg

◆ *Nimbochromis venustus*
(BOULENGER, 1908)

belongs to the larger members of the genus with maximum length records ranging up to nearly 25 centimetres. Adult males and females can be easily distinguished by means of the different colour patterns. Female specimens have an ochre to ivory coloured body with large, irregular, light brown to olive blotches of partly rhomboid shape. These markings have disappeared in males. Their flanks are uniformly curry- to lemon-yellow with head and nape being coloured bright azure- to ultramarine-blue. A golden yellowish stripe extends from the anterior portion of the lip over the forehead and mostly continues in the outer section of the dorsal fin. Juveniles are coloured and patterned like the females.

The

natural habitat

of this Cichlid is the sandy littoral of Lake Malawi. The fish is also regularly en-

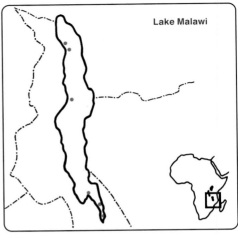

Localities of *Nimbochromis venustus*

countered in the *Vallisneria* meadows. Fully grown specimens mainly feed on other fishes.

Due to the fact that the males are very bright coloured, the species is a very popular aquarium fish, despite its large size.

Male of *Nimbochromis venustus*

The successful

care

obviously calls for large aquaria with a length of approximately one and a half metres. Like most other species from Lake Malawi, *N. venustus* should preferably be kept in a community tank. Adequate company fishes are other large species of *Nimbochromis* as well as hardy Mbuna-cichlids such as *N. polystigma, N. linni, N. livingstonii, Pseudotropheus zebra,* or *Labeotropheus fuelleborni.* Also in the case of this Cichlid, the male should be in the company of several females as a single female would otherwise be harassed too much.

Although *N. venustus* is an inhabitant of the sandy grounds, the decoration of the aquarium should include large stone-plates which divide the floor-space into territories and provide hiding-sites. On account of soft leaves being considered food, only hard or fast-growing plants should be chosen for greening the aquarium. Positive results were achieved, for example, with densely planted Giant Vallisnerias.

An appropriate diet for adult specimens will obviously require rich food and focus on a regular supply with pieces of fish. This may be supplemented by earthworms, TetraCichlid Sticks and shrimp-meat.

Paying attention to the aforesaid basics, the

breeding

of this fish is easy and should be attempted in the community aquarium. Courtship and spawning take place in the manner typical for Haplochromines. This species also belongs to the mouthbrooders which rear their offspring in a mother-family. There is no bonding between the reproduction partners. The caring mother specimen should be isolated shortly before the larval development is completed if it is intended to rear the juveniles. At a water-temperature of 26 °C, the the female should be transferred into a separate tank is approximately the 15th or 16th day after spawning. The juveniles are fairly large and independent. Their rearing is easy on an initial diet of selected small *Daphnia.* Larger females may produce more than 100 juveniles at a time.

The number of species and individuals of Mbuna-cichlids can be surprisingly high. (Littoral of the island of Thumbi at four metres depth).

The most remarkable Cichlids of Lake Tanganyika certainly include the representatives of

the genus Ophthalmotilapia

which was described by PELLEGRIN in 1903. After it was revised by LIEM (1981) and POLL (1986), it now contains four species which have become known amongst aquarists for their unusually enlarged threadlike ventral fins. In fully grown males, these even exceed the posterior edge of the anal fin when pressed against the body.

In male specimens, the end of the ventral fin is forked and the two points are augmented to small lobes whose shapes and colour imitate the eggs of this species. Observations in the natural habitat of this fish revealed that these unusually modified ventral fins play an important role in the courtship and reproduction of this species.

During courtship, the males spread their ventral fins wide from the body and thus display to the females the yellowish coloured lobes which are to be considered fake eggs. These egg dummies on the tips of the ventral fins serve the intraspecific communication and initiate instinctive behavioural patterns amongst the females. *Ophthalmotilapia* are specialized mouthbrooders. During the spawning act the female immediately turns around after a batch of eggs is discharged and takes the eggs into the mouth before the male was able to fertilize them. As soon as the male presents the egg dummies, the female begins to snap after them. On doing so, it picks up the sperm released by the male which then fertilizes the eggs in the mouth of the mother specimen.

The statement that *Ophthalmotilapia* would spawn without direct contact between the reproduction partner which is repeatedly found in the aquaristic literature, is wrong and based on a misinterpretation of the underwater observations made by BRICHARD (1978). I had opportunity to repeatedly watch *Ophthalmotilapia* spawning in their natural habitat (Tanzania, Zambia) whilst diving. In all cases the spawning behaviour was not any different from that of other East African mouthbrooders. These observations were then confirmed by studies on *Ophthalmotilapia ventralis* in the aquarium.

Tanganyika-cichlids can also be found in bays with sandy ground.

◆ *Ophthalmotilapia nasuta*
(POLL & MATTHES, 1962)

males may reach a total length of eighteen centimetres. The identification of the sex is easy in the case of adult specimens due to the presence of a distinct sexual dimorphism.

The upper half of the fish is yellowish grey, the lower more ivory coloured. The flanks are marked with six or seven dark transversal bands. Courting males assume a fairly dark body colouration and a blueish gleam appears on their sides. The caudal fin is deeply forked with the top and bottom rays being enlarged to filaments. The most important feature of the males is the shape of the ventral fins which are extremely enlarged and carry conspicuous yellow lobes at their ends. Females are distinctly lighter in colour and lack the lobes of the ventral fins. Their dorsal, anal, and caudal fins are also less pointed.

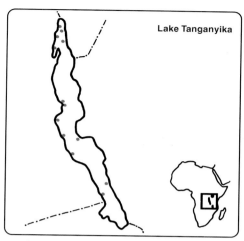

Localities of *Ophthalmotilapia nasuta*

The most obvious feature of this species is a meaty protrusion which overlaps the mouth like a nose. It is more distinct in males than in females.

Male of *Ophthalmotilapia nasuta*

123

The

natural habitat

of *Ophthalmotilapia nasuta* is the rocky zone near the shore. The preferred depth lies between two and fifteen metres. Numerous colour morphs are known to exist in Lake Tanganyika, amongst which is a pure yellow one. Localities have been recorded from Zaïre in the northwest, west, and southwest, and from Tanzania in the east and southeast. It appears that the species is especially common in the northeast (Burundi).

In its natural environment the fish is omnivore. Studies on the stomach contents conducted by the original authors showed that the specimens had fed upon monocellular and filamentous algae, monocellular organisms, insects, and molluscs. The fact that also sand and mud was found in the stomach indicates that the fish primarily feeds on detritus which is taken up from the ground.

Care

The can be problems with keeping this beautiful species for this remarkable Cichlid requires a large aquarium which offers the fish sufficient space for swimming. The minimum length of the tank should therefore be one and a half metres. For a natural decoration one needs rocks which are piled up along the back wall and create a number of dens of different sizes. The ground should preferably consist of sand or very fine gravel. If one does not want to forgo vegetation, one should only choose species with low growth. Plants like *Anubias nana* furthermore have the advantage of anchoring directly on the rocks.

An aquarium of normal dimensions cannot take more than one male with his two or three females. Company fishes should in no way be as nervous and rough as the species of *Tropheus* for example. They would not only bother the *Ophthalmotilapia* through their vivid behaviour, they also will not leave sufficient food for them. More adequate species may be the representatives of the genera *Julidochromis*, *Chalinochromis*, and the moderately sized *Neolamprologus* which are much more peaceful.

Being an omnivore, *Ophthalmotilapia nasuta* can easily be provided with a varying diet. Attention must definitely be paid to the fact that this fairly large fish requires sufficient quantities of food.

The

breeding

has been successful in many cases. A precondition is that the specific requirements are appropriately met. Firstly, this fairly large fish needs sufficient swimming space. Secondly, it also requires an adequate diet. Furthermore, it is important that sand is used as substrate to enable the males to create spawning pits. Finally, these Cichlids cannot be kept together with deliberately chosen company fishes from Lake Tanganyika as they are put under stress by vivid or aggressive fishes, such as *Tropheus* for example.

All *Ophthalmotilapia* are agame mouthbrooders which rear their offspring in a mother-family. Since the eggs are big and contain large amounts of yolk, the juveniles already are of a fair size when they leave the protecting mouth of the mother and can be fed with selected small *Daphnia* and crushed flake-food.

Ophthalmotilapia nasuta is certainly a Cichlid which can only be recommended to the experienced aquarist and which will definitely not become a frequently kept species due to its space requirements. On the other hand, its husbandry promises many interesting observations. The particular function of the yellow tips of the ventral fins was already discussed in the genus account. Provided that the possibility exists to house the fish according to its ecological requirements, its husbandry can be a rewarding challenge for the enthusiastic aquarist.

The Genus

Oreochromis

was already described by GÜNTHER in 1889, but actually became notable only in 1981 when a couple of specialized East and Central African mouthbrooders were included by the English ichthyologist TREWAVAS. These species had formerly been assigned to genera such as *Tilapia* and *Sarotherodon*.

Although *Oreochromis* forms a voluminous systematic unit, it is of minor importance to the aquarists. The reason is that a majority of species reaches such excessive lengths that adult specimens can hardly be kept in normal tanks any more. In contrast, the genus is more important to commercial fisheries, and various members are renowned fishes which are of importance for sustenance of man. Therefore they are bred on large scale in fish-ponds.

▶ Oreochromis mossambicus
(PETERS, 1852)

undoubtedly belongs to the Cichlids most intensely studied by scientists. The surprisingly great interest in this species is indicated by an almost incomprehensive number of publications by representatives of most different biological sub-disciplines. The reason is the importance of this species as an esteemed edible fish in countries of the tropics. Obviously, it is desirable to farm this fish as effective as possible and rear it to a size where it becomes a suitable meal.

Although the fish can grow up to a length of more than thirty-five centimetres under

Male of *Oreochromis mossambicus*

favourable conditions, they are not necessarily out of question for the aquarium since it already matures at a length of ten centimetres. Displaying a distinct sexual dichromatism during times of courtship, adult males and females can easily be distinguished. Sexually active males assume a pitch black colouration on large parts of the body and the fins. The lower portion of the head below the eye between lower lip and the edge of the operculum becomes pearl-white and thus creates a nice contrast. The purely white coloured genital papilla then also becomes very conspicuous. The ventral fins, the outer section of the caudal fin, and the margin of the dorsal fin are coral-red. Outside the breeding seasons the males are merely greenish grey to olive, very much resembling the khaki-coloured females. During times of care for the fry, female specimens display an

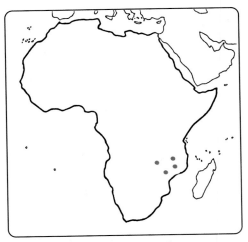

Localities of *Oreochromis mossambicus*

interrupted dark longitudinal stripe which actually consists of five individual blotches.

Female of *Oreochromis mossambicus* with mouthfull of juveniles

The

natural habitats

of this species are formed by rivers, lakes, and swamps in East Africa. The original distribution ranged from northern South Africa to Mozambique, and TREWAVAS (1966) listed the lower part of the Shire River and Zambezi as well as the southern coastal waters down to Algoa Bay as localities. On the other hand, the exact borders of its natural range can hardly be reconstructed since the species has widely been distributed far beyond the originally inhabited area by humans. Due to man's interaction, *Oreochromis mossambicus* has almost become a cosmopolite throughout the tropics. The fish does not only occur in the waters of Africa, but also in America, numerous Asian countries, Madagascar, the West Indies, and the Seychelles. Being extraordinarily hardy with a high potential to adapt, its distribution is not limited by the availability of a certain type of biotope. Thus, it has established itself in the most different types of water-bodies and has fairly dissimilar ecologies. In some areas where the fish has been introduced by man, this Cichlid has become a severe threat to the native ichthyofauna.

The

care

in an aquarium is certainly limited to just matured specimens of about ten centimetres in length. As the fish grows fairly rapidly these half-grown specimens can easily double their length within only one year if provided with a sufficient amount of space and adequate quantities of food. Therefore, aquaria with a length of less than one metre are suitable for this species only for a short time.

The ground of the tank should consist of sand or fine gravel. By utilizing a few flat stones the floor-space should be sectioned in such a manner that the fish can easily define the borders of their territories. Since

O. mossambicus occasionally nips on delicate shoots, only tough or fast-growing plants are suitable for further decoration. Planting should only be along the rear and side walls so that as much floor-space as possible remains unobstructed. It is strongly recommended to place some large stones around the roots of the plants to prevent the fish from digging them out during their preparation works for spawning.

Oreochromis mossambicus is not only relatively tolerant towards other Cichlids, but also towards other male conspecifics. Despite greatly ritualized combats about the definition or the maintenance of territorial borders, damaging fights are generally forgone. The most interesting observations are made when several males are kept together with a larger number of females in a spacious aquarium of more than one metre in length. The males then display a so-called "arena-behaviour" by dividing the floor-space amongst themselves and each one creating a shallow spawning-pit. These courtship and spawning territories are defended against all neighbours in combat fights. As soon as a female becomes ready to spawn, all males attempt to lure it into their own spawning-pit and to mate with her. Provided with a floor-space of half a square metre approximately five males of ten centimetres in length are able to define their territories.

Oreochromis mossambicus has a great ability to adapt, is very robust, and can also be recommended to the beginner. It tolerates water-temperatures between 20 and 30 °C and eagerly feeds on everything offered.

As can be perceived from the preceding details, no special efforts need be undertaken for the

breeding

of this fish. It is an agame mouthbrooder which rears its offspring in a mother-family. Large females lay about a thousand eggs, small ones about one hundred.

The Genus Paracyprichromis

POLL, 1986

At the first glance, the layman would hardly ever identify these slender fishes of Lake Tanganyika to be Cichlids at all. Despite their unusual appearance the *Paracyprichromis* species are nevertheless typical Cichlids with highly interesting behavioural patterns which make them recommendable objects to study in the aquarium.

These Cichlids are known to ichthyology since 1898. However, it was not before 1977 that a separate genus — *Cyprichromis* — was established for them which took into consideration their variuous peculiarities. The ichthyologist POLL eventually transferred two of these species to another new genus — *Paracyprichromis* — in 1986. Although all the species of these two genera resemble each other closely, both these groups differ considerably with regard to their ecologies and behavioural patterns. At present, the genus *Paracyprichromis* accommodates only the two species *P. nigripinnis* and *P. brieni*.

The surprising fact that, despite their highly decorative colour and interesting behavioural patterns, these Cichlids have been discovered for the aquaristic so late, is based on their ecology. As these fishes have very specific habitat preferences which are only present on a few isolated locations on the shores of the lake and generally occur at deeper levels, they are difficult to find or to observe and almost impossible to catch without scuba-diving equipment. Depending on the species, the top range of their distribution lies between three and fifteen metres. *P. nigripinnis* appears to prefer greater depths whilst *P. brieni* was also repeatedly observed in the upper littoral.

All Cypri-cichlids specialize on certain prey. In their natural habitats, they feed on plankton, occupying a very similar ecological niche in Lake Tanganyika as the species of *Copadichromis* do in Lake Malawi. However, this sort of resemblance is no indication of a close cladistic relationship, but must be interpreted as a convergence induced by comparable ecologies.

Cape Nundo in the Sumbu National Park (Lake Tanganyika)

◆ *Paracyprichromis nigripinnis*
(BOULENGER, 1091)

Although this Cichlid belongs to the fishes known from Lake Tanganyika for a long time, first live imports were not observed before 1989. All aquaristic reports on this fish published before this date do not refer to this species, but to *Paracyprichromis brieni*.

Like all other Cypri-cichlids, *Paracyprichromis nigripinnis* also has a slender, elongate bodyshape. As an adaption to its special ecology as plankton feeder, the fish is able to widely protrude its flexible mouth. The background colouration of the males is brown with the head and flanks being marked with three intensely blue coloured longitudinal stripes. The dorsal fin is yellowish and patterned with two longitudinal rows of blue spots. It is furthermore bordered with blue on its upper margin and marked with a narrow blue line on its base. The ventral, anal, and caudal fins are blackish, but also have blue margins. The

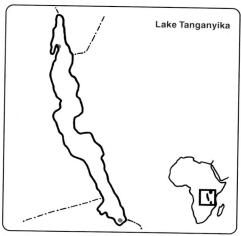

Localities of *Paracyprichromis nigripinnis*

females look very much the same, but their colour patterns are lighter with the blue shining stripes being considerably paler.

The sexes can be distinguished by the females lacking the bifurcate caudal fin typical to the males. The ventral fins and the posterior edges of the dorsal and anal fins

Male of *Paracyprichromis nigripinnis*

are not rounded as in male specimens but pointed.

The maximum length of *Paracyprichromis nigripinnis* is approximately ten centimetres. Females do not reach this size.

The

natural habitat

of *Paracyprichromis nigripinnis* is the lower rocky littoral at depths below twenty metres. Here, the Cichlid preferably lives socially in larger group along steep coasts in the immediate vicinity of vertical rockfaces. They apparently do not migrate but are consistent to a specific location.

All *Paracyprichromis* feed on plankton including not only the small shrimps of the *Cyclops*-group but also planktonic algae. A distinct adaption to this food is the flexible mouth that can be protruded like a pipe. As can be observed when fed with the nauplii of the Brine Shrimp, this operates like a sucking organ. Based on the feeding habits of the fish it may be presumed that the Cypri-cichlids of Lake Tanganyika accumulate and reside along the steep coasts because the current provides them with their prey there.

The presently known localities of *Para-cyprichromis nigripinnis* lie in the extreme south of Lake Tanganyika in the Chituta Bay (KONINGS 1988) and in the northwest on the Ubwari Peninsula. Reports about its occurrence in northern Tanzania still require confirmation.

Care

There can be problems with keeping this remarkable species. To suit this Cichlid a spacious aquarium is required. By means of sand and stone-plates it should be decorated to form an imitation of the rocky littoral. The usage of plants should be sparse so that the space for swimming is not reduced. It is noteworthy that *Paracyprich-romis nigripinnis* requires larger grottos to feel at ease. The specimens can often be seen swimming upside down on the ceiling of

these. All species should be kept in groups of several males and females. *P. nigripinnis* needs a lot of space. It is territorial and maintains comparatively large territories which are defended against conspecifics.

Special attention must be paid to the cleanliness of the water and to the diet. It appears as though all species depend on a regular supply with live small shrimps, e.g. *Cyclops* or *Artemia salina*. If kept in con-taminated water and on an exclusive diet of flake-food, the fish may become blind. Adequate company fishes with whom these Cichlids can be kept together are especially found amongst the smaller members of the genera *Neolamprologus* and *Julidochromis*. Very active and aggressive species are inap-propriate for this purpose.

The

breeding

of these Cichlids is in no way a problem, if the husbandry conditions and diet are suit-able for the species. All forms are maternal mouthbrooders which means that the eggs are taken into the mouth by the female immediately upon being released and incu-bated there. Even when exposed to increased temperatures, it takes more than four weeks until the juveniles are spat out by the mother due to the fact that the eggs are large and contain a lot of yolk. At this stage, the young fish measure already twelve mil-limetres.

Studies in the aquarium showed that the members of the genus *Paracyprichromis* spawn on a substrate whereas those of *Cyprichromis* spawn in the open water. *Para-cyprichromis nigripinnis* preferably spawns on vertical rockfaces. For this purpose the female positions herself with the head down and waits until the released egg sinks between the fish's body and the rockface and reaches the mouth where it is sucked in. Even during periods of mouthbrooding, the females take up food. They should regularly be offered newly hatched nauplii of the Brine Shrimp *(Artemia salina)*.

The Genus

Petrochromis

was introduced by BOULENGER in 1898. Its distribution is confined to Lake Tanganyika. To date, not more than six species have scientifically been described, but quite a few more species are known that still await formal descriptions. Amongst the fishes living on the lawn of algae in Lake Tanganyika, *Petrochromis* are the most specialized. Being strictly bound to a rocky ground, most species occur in relatively isolated populations. Obviously, this isolation has favoured the development of different colour varieties, and in this respect *Petrochromis* resembles the genus *Tropheus*. However, whilst relatively detailed knowledge has been gathered of the representatives of the genus *Tropheus* because their conspicuous colour patterns make them popular fishes for the aquarium, the generally fairly drab coloured *Petrochromis* are poorly known.

▶ *Petrochromis polyodon*
BOULENGER, 1898

may reach a maximum length of approximately twenty centimetres. The identification of the sexes is fairly easy in the case of adult specimens as there is a distinct sexual dichromatism. The body of a fully coloured male is copper-red to beige-brown with a blueish colour-zone appearing on the forehead between the upper edge of the eyes and the upper lip. The ventral fins and the anterior portion of the dorsal fin are reddish orange to orange-brown whilst its posterior part and the caudal fin are blueish grey. In adult males, three to four small oval yellowish spots bordered with black are visible on the anal fin. In contrast, female specimens are considerably paler and their ventral, dorsal, and anal fins are less pointed.

The described colour pattern refers to specimens from the vicinity of Kigoma (Tanzania). Those originating from Zambia have a striped pattern.

Petrochromis polyodon from Kigoma

The

natural habitat

of this fish is the shallow rubble-zone near the shore. Locality records have been made in the vicinity of Kigoma (Tanzania), in the south (Zambia), and along the west coast (Zaïre). The source of food is the lawn of algae which covers the stones and boulders which they graze upon assisted by the flexible and densely toothed mouth.

To make its

care

successful, this Cichlid ought to be kept only in aquaria exceeding one metre in length. It appears to be not recommendable to keep this fish on its own as it is very aggressive towards conspecifics. The intraspecific aggression is reduced to a certain extend through the presence of other fishes in a community tank. These company fishes should primarily be chosen from similarly hardy and active species.

A naturally decorated aquarium must provide a multitude of alcoves and sanctuaries which are created by stones and stone-plates. Plants do not appear to be really adequate as *P. polyodon* nibbles on delicate leaves and shoots. The diet of this fish should vary between several types of flake-food, mosquito larvae and *Daphnia*. Food-items poor in fibres, e.g. worms, are not really appropriate for this specialized vegetarian.

The

breeding

should take place in the community aquarium described above. *P. polyodon* is an agame mouthbrooder, thus the males must be kept together with a large harem. Due to the eggs being very large and containing a lot of yolk, the development of the larvae takes fairly long. At a water-temperature around 26 °C, approximately four weeks will pass until the mother releases the fry

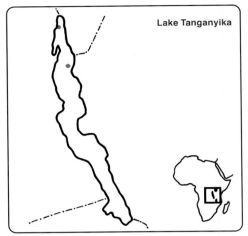

Localities of *Petrochromis polyodon*

from the mouth for the first time. At this stage, the young fish already measure more than ten millimetres and are capable of feeding on small *Daphnia* and crushed flake-food. In a naturally decorated community aquarium free of predatory fishes, the young *Petrochromis polyodon* will grow up without considerable losses.

Even a soft breeze causes a strong surf in Lake Tanganyika.

The Genus Placidochromis

ECCLES & TREWAVAS, 1989

is endemic to Lake Malawi and Lake Malombe. It is characterized by a distinct pattern of stripes. Out of the seven species only three are known to the aquaristic hobby.

▶ *Placidochromis johnstoni*

(GÜNTHER, 1893)

For this species, a maximum length of 17 centimetres has been recorded, but under aquarium conditions the fish remain distinctly smaller. Due to a clearly developed sexual dichromatism, males and females can easily be distinguished. Males ready for reproduction are quite brightly coloured with the head, but also the rest of the body, being overlain by a metallic shining turquoise-blue. On a light blue ground, the dorsal and caudal fins have a pattern of deep

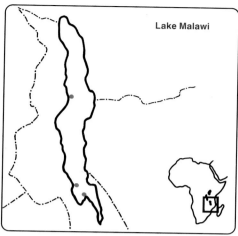

Localities of *Placidochromis johnstoni*

reddish purple oval speckles. Six dark transversal bands mark the flanks between the edge of the operculum and the caudal fin.

Females and juveniles also display these bands, but their bodies are inconspicuously yellowish grey to greenish beige.

Male of *Placidochromis johnstoni*

The
natural habitats
of this Cichlid lie in the sandy littoral of Lake Malawi. Preferred places to reside are the thickets of Vallisnerias which may virtually extend to underwater pastures. Within the lake, the fish is widely distributed and relatively common.

The long-term
care
should be attempted in a large community aquarium with a minimum length of one metre. An adequate range of company fishes is found amongst other Haplochromines, e.g. Mbuna-cichlids of the genera *Pseudotropheus* or *Labeotropheus*. The floor-space need to be clearly sectioned by rock-construction that also serve as hiding-sites. Only tough plants should be used for greening the tank as *P. johnstoni* occasionally nibbles on delicate young shoots. Fast growing plants also survive occasional damage. A dense group of Giant Vallisnerias is therefore a good choice for greening the aquarium. The ground should consist of coarse sand or fine gravel that need to be thoroughly rinsed before usage.

Feeding this fish is no problem at all. *Daphnia*, insect larvae, fishmeat and shrimps (deep-sea shrimps), but also flake-food such as TetraCichlid or TetraMin are readily accepted.

In this case the
breeding
should also take place in the community tank where the female can avoid the consistent pursuits of the male. *P. johnstoni* is a specialized mouthbrooder which rears its offspring in a mother-family.

A male ready to spawn excavates a bowl-like pit in the centre of its territory in which the spawning takes places. By trembling and subsequently guiding it to the spawning-site, the female is attracted. The

spawning act follows the pattern typical for most of the East African mouthbrooders.

At water-temperatures around 26 °C, the young fish are released from the mouth for the first time after two to three weeks. This species is fairly productive and larger females may incubate more than onehundred juveniles. Even after the fry swims freely, the mother keeps on protecting and defending it. During the night, the young fish return into her shielding mouth.

Despite the intense care, juveniles will only grow up in exceptional cases if left in the community aquarium. Their inherited behaviour is not fit to survive under such circumstances. The breeder will therefore be forced to prepare a separate tank into which the caring mother specimen can be transferred when it comes close to the point where the juveniles are spat out for the first time. Initially, the young fish are reared on a diet of nauplii of the Brine Shrimp *(Artemia salina)* and powder-food; later with selected small *Daphnia*.

Vegetation zone of Lake Malawi at two metres depth (Cape Maclear)

◗ *Placidochromis milomo*
(OLIVER, 1989)

This conspicuous fish, of which differently coloured populations exist, has long since known to aquarists. Due to the fact that its formal scientific description was not published before 1989, a valid species name was not available for a long time and the fish was often allocated to the genus *Melanochromis*.

As the scientific species name indicates — the word "milomo" means lips in the Chichewa language — this Cichlid belongs to a group of fishes which all share the feature of greatly enlarged lips that often have a hook-like protrusion. Surprisingly enough this peculiar characteristic is no general sign of a closer systematic relationship but has independently developed in several ichthyological regions on various continents. Cichlids with such curious lips are not unique to Lake Malawi, but also occur in Lake Tanganyika, Lake Victoria, and even in Lake Nicaragua in Central America.

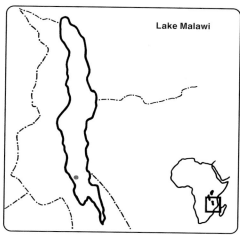

Locality of *Placidochromis milomo* (Mbenji variety)

Lake Malawi is home to several forms with enlarged lips like this which otherwise differ considerably regarding their colour patterns. Whether these are separate species or just colour morphs of one and the same

Semi-adult male of *Placidochromis milomo*, Mbenji variety

species has yet to be investigated. The allocation to the taxon *Placidochromis milomo* of the Cichlid described in the following is therefore made with certain reservations and may only be temporarily.

The fish reaches a length exceeding eighteen centimetres. The identification of the sexes is easy due to the existence of a clear sexual dichromatism. Juveniles and females have an orange-brown to brownish beige ground colouration and carry five broad dark transversal bands between the edge of the operculum and the base of the caudal fin. Another such band extends over the gill-cover onto the nape. Males are characterized by the upper half of the head being metallic azure-blue whereas the lower portion is turquoise. Courting males assume a blueish green colouration all over the body so that they appear more or less uniformly coloured.

The

natural habitat

of this fish seems to be restricted to the southern half of lake Malawi since localities have to date only been recorded from the southeastern and southwestern corners of the lake, i.e. from Nkhata Bay and the islands of Mbenji and Likoma. Since the fish is relatively rare, little data exists about its ecology. Controversial opinions exist, for example, about the function and the biological importance of the enlarged lips. One hypothesis is that the fish would feed on the lawn of algae and that the lips would be furnished with a very high number of nerve-cells serving as probing organs that simplify the detection of insect larvae and other small prey. Another presumption is that the fish may use the thick lips to shut narrow rock-crevices in order to suck prey out of their hiding placed.

Care

Since this Cichlid grows to a fair size, the maintenance of adult specimens makes aquaria of more than a metre in length necessary. The natural decoration includes rocks between which alcoves and caves are available and which enable the definition of separate territories.

An optimally assembled group will consist of one male and two to three females. The species is fairly vigorous and knows how to effectively resist aggressive company fishes. Therefore, not only larger species of *Nimbochromis* make appropriate coinhabitants, but also the energetic Mbuna-cichlids of the genera *Pseudotropheus*, *Melanochromis*, and *Labeotropheus*.

Hardy and resistive plants are usually not damaged, but in order not to further limit the available space, one should only choose plants which anchor directly on the rock-constructions. This will favour the West African species of *Anubias* and the Javanese Fern *Microsorum pteropus*.

Feeding this Cichlid is quite easy as virtually all common types of food are accepted. One should however be aware of the fact that fully grown specimens feed on large items and depend on powerful food. The keeper should therefore focus on pieces of fish, shrimps, earthworms, and Tetra-Cichlid Sticks.

The

breeding

takes place in the community aquarium. As in all Haplochromines of Lake Malawi, this species is also a specialized mouthbrooder which rears its fry in a mother-family. At a water-temperature of around 26 °C, the development of the eggs and larvae takes nearly three weeks.

If necessary, the breeding female can be removed from the community tank shortly before this period has elapsed and transferred to a separate aquarium of its own where it may complete its maternal care undisturbed.

The juveniles are relatively large and can be fed with selected small *Daphnia* and crushed flake-food.

The Genus *Protomelas*

ECCLES & TREWAVAS, 1989

This genus accommodates fourteen taxo-nomically revised species. Out of these, only three or four have achieved relevance as popular aquarium fishes to date. In addition, there are some more species whose scientific description is still outstanding. The species of *Protomelas* have a dark banded pattern in which up to two longitudinal stripes are overlain by a number of transversal bands.

▶ *Protomelas* sp.

"Steveni tiger"

This splendid Cichlid has repeatedly been assigned to the species *Protomelas taeniola-tus*. However, on the basis of present knowledge this is nothing but a presump-tion which is yet to be verified.

In contrast to the brightly coloured males, the juveniles and the females of this species have a silvery to grey ground col-ouration and one or two dark longitudinal

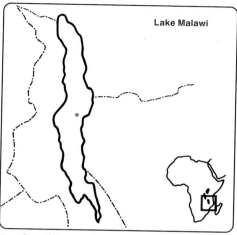

Locality of *Protomelas* sp. "Steveni tiger"

stripes that are overlain by up to twelve nar-row transversal bands. The head, as well as the dorsal and caudal fins of the males appear in a bright ultramarine blue. The flanks are deep yellow anteriorly and curry-yellow in the posterior portion. The caudal fin is patterned with irregular, brownish red, longitudinal stripes with the

Male of *Protomelas* sp. "Steveni tiger"

posteriormost part being marked with oval spots of the same colour.

Males are usually imported at lengths of approximately nine centimetres, but may subsequently grow up to twelve centimetres in the aquarium at home.

The rocky zone near the shore forms the

natural habitat

of this Cichlid. The sole locality known to date is the littoral of the islands of Likoma and Chisumulu which both lie in the central part of Lake Malawi. The males are usually seen swimming above a larger boulder with a horizontal surface that forms the centre of their territories. The preferred depth of the water appears to be three to ten metres.

The fish has a fairly small mouth. Although it not really feeds on the lawn of algae that covers rocks and boulders, the microinhabitants of this lawn appears to be its most important source of sustenance.

The

care

is not difficult and highly recommendable. It is a peace-loving species. Being fairly active and requiring adequate space for swimming the aquarium should measure more than one metre in length. As observed by the author, the females are rarely pursued by the males. Housed in a community tank of two metres in length it was no problem to keep this Cichlid in a pair. Co-inhabitants must not be aggressive, but should preferably be small species of *Copadichromis, Aulonocara,* and *Trematocranus.*

A natural decoration of the tank is achieved by arranging large stones and rocks to form caves and crevices. Since the fish completely ignores plants, the aquarium can also be greened. But the plants should not limit the available space, and one should preferably only choose species which grow low or anchor on the rocks.

The fish feeds on small sized prey, but willingly accepts all common types of food.

A varying diet should consist of *Daphnia,* White Mosquito larvae, grated shrimp-meat (deep-sea shrimps), TetraMin, or TetraCichlid.

The community aquarium is a suitable place for

breeding

this Haplochromine. It is a mouthbrooder which does not develop a bonding between the reproduction partners. The female alone cares for the fry. At a water-temperature of 26 °C, the development of the juveniles is far advanced after nearly three weeks, and the mother releases them from the mouth for the first time. At this stage, they can be fed with MikroMin, newly hatched nauplii of the Brine Shrimp, and also selected small *Daphnia* and crushed TetraMin.

After eight weeks the young fish may have already grown to thirty millimetres.

Male of the *Protomelas fenestratus*-group in its breeding territory at five metres depth

The Genus

Pseudocrenilabrus

Based on behavioural studies, WICKLER (1963) came to the conclusion that two species which had formerly been included in the genus *Haplochromis* would better be accommodated in a separate genus which he named *Hemihaplochromis*.

TREWAVAS (1977) then drew notice to the fact that one of these two species, i.e. *Chromis philander* WEBER, 1897, had erroneously been described once again as a new species under the name of *Pseudocrenilabrus natalensis* by FOWLER in 1934. By an older name having priority for a younger one according to the nomenclatural rules, WICKLER'S generic name thus became invalid.

At present, the genus *Pseudocrenilabrus* incorporates three species after BANNISTER & BAILEY (1979) also allocated *P. nicholsi* (PELLEGRIN, 1928) to this unit.

▶ *Pseudocrenilabrus multicolor victoriae*

SEEGERS, 1990

Males of this species reach approximately eight centimetres in length whereas females generally remain smaller. The identification is simplified by the fact that a distinct sexual dichromatism is present. Male specimens are considerably more splendid than females with the body having a lemon- to cadmium-yellow metallic gleam. The light blue colouration of the lips is quite noteworthy, and the same tone of colour also appears on the posterior half of the body and in the form of a spotted pattern on all unpairy fins. The posterior margin of the anal fin is deep orange or even fire-red in colour.

This pretty Cichlid has long been known to aquarists, but was erroneously referred to as *Pseudocrenilabrus philander dispersus* until formally and scientifically described in 1990.

Male of *Pseudocrenilabrus multicolor victoriae*

The

natural distribution

of this subspecies is fairly wide and extends over the entire catchment area of the upper Nile and Lake Victoria, i.e. covers the west and the south of Uganda, Kenya, and the northwest of Tanzania. The fish mainly inhabits swampy areas, streams, shallow bays, and dead side-arms of larger rivers which are densely vegetated.

P. multicolor victoriae is an extraordinarily hardy Cichlid with a great ability to adapt. It neither calls for a special quality of water nor special food, thus its

care

is easy. It is one of the mouthbrooders recommendable for the beginner and even an aquarium of half a metre in length can already be adequate. It cannot be kept in pairs, but a male must be supplied with a small harem. Being sexually active constantly, the males otherwise pursue the females too much. A larger tank may even be home to two or three males if these can separate their individual territories from one another.

This Cichlid is plant-tolerant and also feels home in an aquarium with a relatively dense vegetation! Separate thickets of plants are even a prerequisite for its successful keeping as they provide shelter and cover for the females during period of maternal care and otherwise serve as border marks for the territories of the males.

When decorating the aquarium it must be borne in mind that the excavation of a small spawning pit is part of the males' preparations for courtship. It must therefore be ensured that the ground consists of sand or fine gravel and that there are a few unobstructed interspaces which the males may consider the centres of their territories.

Pseudocrenilabrus multicolor victoriae is tolerant towards other fishes. Co-inhabitants of the aquarium can therefore be other Cichlids as well as representatives of other fish families.

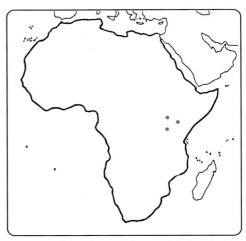

Localities of *Pseudocrenilabrus multicolor victoriae*

The

breeding

can take place in the community tank as well as in a species aquarium if these are decorated according to the preceding information. *P. multicolor victoriae* is a mouthbrooder with no bonding between the reproduction partners. Immediately after the spawning act is finalized, males and females go their own ways, and it is only the mother which cares for the fry.

The courtship of the males is very vivid with important stages being trembling, guiding the female, and the excavation of the spawning pit. The eggs are still unfertilized when the female takes them into her mouth. Their fertilization takes places when the female follows the male with her mouth close to his urogenital region whilst the latter slides over the ground of the spawning pit with the anterior body slightly lifted and releases sperm which the female then takes up. The orange-red posterior lower corner of the male's anal fin obviously plays an important role in the fertilization process. At this stage, the folded seam of this fin forms a conspicuous colourspot that attracts the female's attention and thus ensures that it moves its mouth into the cloud of sperm released by the male fish.

In case of *P. multicolor victoriae,* this anal fin tip can however not be referred to as an egg dummy as the eggs have a completely different colour than the border of the fin.

Adequate husbandry temperatures range between 23 and 28 °C. One should however be aware of the fact that the higher the prevailing temperature the shorter is the period required for the development of the fry. At 28 °C the juveniles are already released from the mouth of the mother after two weeks, but even thereafter the mouthbrooding care is still continued for some time. The juveniles are omnivore and can be fed with the nauplii of the Brine Shrimp, selected small *Daphnia,* and crushed flake-food without problems.

The Genus

Pseudotropheus

was established by REGAN in 1921 and is of great importance to the aquaristic pasttime. It contains some of the most brilliantly coloured Cichlids we know. Besides fishes with conspicuous striking colour patterns, this systematic unit also incorporates several species with more drab appearances which are therefore of less interest for the husbandry in an aquarium. The distribution of this genus is confined to Lake Malawi. More than 130 species and subspecies have been described to date, with this figure constantly rising as new forms never seen before are discovered continually. Aquarists also know of at least a dozen forms whose scientific evaluation is yet to be undertaken.

It is typical for many species of *Pseudotropheus* that they do not occur in all suitable habitats the lake has to offer, but partly inhabit surprisingly small areas that, in extreme cases, hardly exceed the size of a soccerfield. This remarkable phenomenon must be seen in conjunction with the ecology of these Cichlids. *Pseudotropheus* are typical Mbuna-cichlids, i.e. they have specialized on the lawn of algae that covers the upper rubble- and rocky zone with all its plant material and micro-organisms as source of food.

Even their behavioural biology is so greatly adapted to this particular environment that most species cannot survive above sandy ground without rubble or rocks. Consequently, they avoid even moderately sized sandy sections. Due to this reason, Mbuna-cichlids are distributed over the littoral of their lake in many populations which have nearly no contact to one another or are completely isolated. In cases of widely distributed species, this isolation has subsequently led to the derivation of several geographical races, and has eventually, in extremely isolated areas such as the shores of remote islands, resulted in the evolution of new species.

Pseudocrenilabrus multicolor preferably inhabits swampy areas and shallow bays that often have a dense vegetation.

As the scientific description of

◗ *Pseudotropheus lombardoi*
BURGESS, 1977

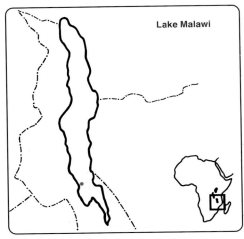

Locality of *Pseudotropheus lombardoi*

is of a fairly recent date, many aquarists still refer to this popular Cichlid under its former trade name of *Pseudotropheus "liliancinius"*. Amongst the Mbuna-cichlids, this species is remarkable in so far that its distinct sexual dichromatism is in awkward contrast to the common standard of the other Mbuna-cichlids. In numerous species of *Pseudotropheus* and *Melanochromis,* but also in the case of the two species of *Labeotropheus,* the males are blue and the females are yellow or orange. In contrast to this, the males of *Pseudotropheus lombardoi* are bright cadmium-yellow whilst the females are azure-blue with a pattern of six dark transversal bands that extend up onto the dorsal fin.

An interesting phenomenon, whose biological importance and origin could not yet be determined, is the fact that some of the female specimens at advanced age assume a colour pattern that closely resembles that of the males. They are then dirty brownish beige to ochre or curry-yellow. This change of colour has certainly nothing to do with a change of sex as those specimens are still able to reproduce like ordinary females. This peculiarity is also known in the genus *Melanochromis.*

Female of *Pseudotropheus lombardoi*

Under aquarium conditions, males may grow up to a length of near fifteen centimetres. It appears that they reach greater sizes in captivity than in their

natural habitat

where they hardly ever exceed eleven centimetres. This species has a surprisingly small range limited to the littoral of the small Mbenji Island. Here, they inhabit the rubble- and rocky zone and sustain themselves on the lawn of algae.

Care

Keeping this pretty Cichlid is only possible in an aquarium not shorter than one and a half metres. One of the more unpleasant attributes of this species is that the specimens are extraordinarily unsocial and aggressive towards their own kind. This does not only apply to the males, but also to the females.

Therefore, it is not recommendable to keep this species on its own. It requires a community aquarium where the presence of other fishes serves as distraction and thus reduces the intraspecific aggression to an acceptable measure.

Unfortunately P. lombardoi becomes also aggressive towards other fishes if the aquarium does not provide sufficient space. The males claim fairly large territories which they bravely defend. Without hesitation they even attack the hand of the keeper if he puts it into the water to work inside the tank. Co-inhabitants of such aquarium must therefore be robust Cichlids such as species of Melanochromis, Labeotropheus fuelleborni, or other Pseudotropheus (P. elongatus, P. zebra).

When decorating the tank, it should be undertaken to emulate the conditions of the rocky zone as closely as possible. Rocks and stoneplates are arranged in such a manner that a multitude of caves and crevices of different sizes are created. These rock-constructions must be piled up to just below the water surface, but must also section the floor-space.

Although plants do not correspond with the natural setting, hardy species can be chosen for the decoration. However, Pseudotropheus lombardoi occasionally nibbles on delicate shoots. As in the case with most of the other Mbuna-cichlids, feeding this fish is no problem. The different types of flake-food are eagerly taken. Obviously, the diet should vary. The bright yellow colours that newly imported males show depends apparently on a supply of carotin-containing food-items, so that small shrimps should be regularly offered.

As far as

breeding

is concerned, one should be aware of the fact that these agame mouthbrooders do not develop a bonding between the reproduction partners. Therefore, a male should be kept together with several females. A breeding attempt will most probably only be successful in the community aquarium described above. Spawning takes place on a flat stone. In a naturally decorated tank a part of the juveniles will grow up without special endeavours. If it is intended to rear the fry completely, the female carrying the clutch should be transferred to a separate aquarium two weeks after spawning. At a water-temperature of approximately 27 °C, the larval development is completed after some three weeks.

Juvenile specimens look very attractive and show the bright blue of the female colouration right from the beginning. The serious breeder should forgo using females which show the unattractive brownish yellow colours in order to avoid a distribution of a possible genetic fault. As the young fish already measure more than ten millimetres when they leave the mouth of the mother, they can easily be fed with small Daphnia and crushed flake-food.

◗ *Pseudotropheus socolofi*

JOHNSON, 1974

Juveniles of this species have a relatively slender and elongate body shape and initially resemble *Pseudotropheus elongatus*, but older specimens become fairly high-backed. The maximum length is twelve centimetres. In contrast to the majority of Malawi-Cichlids, this species has no distinct sexual dichromatism.

Both sexes are light blue with markings being restricted to broad blueish black margins on the outer edges of the ventral fins as well as the dorsal and anal fins. The caudal fin has a striped pattern of the same colour. Whilst territorial males are uniformly coloured, females may show eight to nine indistinct dark transversal bands on the flanks. Males can primarily be identified by having three to four yellow egg dummies bordered with black on their anal fins. Furthermore, their ventral fins are distinctly longer than those of the females.

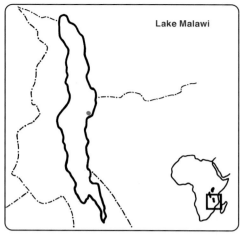

Locality of *Pseudotropheus socolofi*

Today, this species is rarely seen in aquaria since imports have stopped. The reason for this is that its

natural habitat

lies on the eastern shore of Lake Malawi, opposite the island of Likoma, on Mozam-

Male of *Pseudotropheus socolofi*

bican territory. This country has stopped exports of ornamental fish. The species is exclusive to the upper zone of the rubble- and rocky littoral. Like all other *Pseudotropheus* they feed on the lawn of algae.

The

care

should preferably take place in a community aquarium that also houses some other Malawi-cichlids. As *Pseudotropheus socolofi* is in comparison with other representatives of this genus — fairly peaceful and social, a tank of approximately one metre in length ought to be sufficient. A male should have several females available.

In order to create a suitable environment for this fish, the decoration should focus on an adequate number of hiding-places and caves. A modest vegetation which does not limit the available swimming-space too much is possible as this Cichlid is plant-tolerant if hardy species are utilized.

Pseudotropheus socolofi does not feed on big pieces of food. A varying diet should be ensured and consist of *Cyclops, Daphnia,* White Mosquito larvae, and the various

types of flakefood such as TetraPhyll, Tetra-Cichlid, or TetraMin.

No special preparations are necessary for the

breeding

which means no separate breeding-tank is necessary. In a naturally decorated aquarium, this Cichlid will willingly begin to reproduce. If required, the female may be transferred to a separate aquarium shortly before the mouthbrooding care is finalized so that the complete fry can get bigger without losses. This point of time is reached approximately fourteen days after spawning at temperatures around 27 °C.

Like all other members of the genus, *P. socolofi* belongs to the mouthbrooders which rear their offspring in a mother-family. However, as soon as the juveniles are released from the mouth, the care soon comes to an end and the young fish seek cover in rock crevices. They do not show any intention to return to the mouth of the mother. Providing them with selected small *Daphnia* and crushed flake-food, they will be easy to rear.

Rocky littoral of Likoma Island

The problems in the taxonomy and systematics of many Malawi-cichlids can be demonstrated in the case of

▶ *Pseudotropheus tropheops*
REGAN, 1921

Two subspecies have been described, i.e. *Pseudotropheus tropheops gracilior* TREWAVAS, 1935, and *P. tropheops romandi* COLOMBÉ, 1979. Together with the three species *Pseudotropheus novemfasciatus* REGAN, 1921, *P. microstoma* TREWAVAS, 1935, and *P. macrophthalmus* AHL, 1927, the three subspecies of *Pseudotropheus tropheops* form a group of Cichlids which resemble each other very closely and are thus difficult to distinguish. The intense research in the ichthyofauna of Lake Malawi of the past years has shown that this group of allied species probably contains more than 40 forms. RIBBINK and co-authors (1983) assigned not less than 34 forms to the *Pseudotropheus tropheops*-complex whereby they limited their survey to the west and

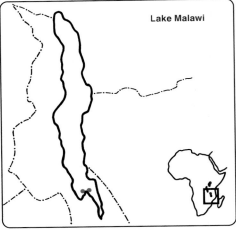

Localities of *Pseudotropheus tropheops* "intermediate"

south of the lake. All members of this species-group are recognizable by the shape of the head. The mouth is low-set with a slightly shorter lower jaw and the forehead is steep, almost vertical.

Female of *Pseudotropheus tropheops* "intermediate"

Female of *Pseudotropheus tropheops* in the rocky littoral of Thumbi Island

Males of the *P. tropheops*-group in the transitory zone from the rocky to the sandy littoral (Dombwe Island, two metres deep)

Observations in the biotope indicate that the members of the *Pseudotropheus tropheops*-complex may be good species in most cases. Important support for this presumption is obtained from the fact that the members of the *tropheops*-complex partly have very different ecological requirements and thus inhabit different biotopes. Besides inhabitants of the rubble- and rocky zone, there are other forms which are exclusive to the transitory zone from the rubble- to the sandy littoral or only occur in the reed-belt. Unfortunately, most of the Cichlids of the *tropheops*-complex cannot be distinguished by the aquarist as the existing identification features are not suitable for the determination of live specimens. However, a revision of the entire group is under way.

A shared trait of all forms of the *tropheops*-complex is the colouration being always yellow or beige in female specimens, while it usually varies between blue tones in males. In the case of *Pseudotropheus tropheops*, the females and juveniles have a bright cadmium-yellow colouration whereas the males are usually khaki-grey to ochre-brownish. A metallic blueish shine overlays this background colouration on the flanks. During courtship they often assume

a blueish black colour. In the aquarium, they may nearly reach thirteen centimetres in length.

The

natural habitat

of this Cichlid is the transitory zone from the rocky to the sandy littoral. Confirmed locality records are exclusive to the southern part of Lake Malawi. The specimen illustrated here was caught in the vicinity of Cape Maclear. Like the other representatives of the genus, *P. tropheops* finds its food in the lawn of algae.

An adequate

care

calls for an aquarium of at least one metre in length. Positive experiences were made when this species was kept in a community tank together with other Malawi-cichlids, whilst it is not recommendable to keep it in a separate aquarium on its own. *Pseudotropheus tropheops* is not really an aggressive fish and it is even fairly tolerant towards conspecifics. It is neverthless impossible to house more than one adult male in one aquarium. Two to three females should be company enough.

The decoration of the aquarium should largely imitate the natural environment. Most important decoration items are therefore stones and pieces of rock which are arranged to form caves and crevices of various sizes. Using hard species of plant, it is possible to green the aquarium to a certain extent, but it should be ensured that sufficient swimming-space remains.

Feeding this fish is not a problem as all common types of food are readily accepted. In order to make it as varying as possible, *Daphnia*, insect larvae, and the various types of flake-food should be offered alternatingly.

As in the case of most other Mbuna-cichlids, the

breeding

should preferably take place in the community aquarium. Provided with a natural decoration of the tank, a few juveniles will grow up from every clutch without particular precautions. *Pseudotropheus tropheops* is an agame mouthbrooder which rears its offspring in a mother-family.

At water-temperatures around 27 °C it takes about three weeks from spawning to the first appearance of the juveniles. The motherly care ends soon afterwards. The fry are reared on a diet of selected tiny *Daphnia* and powdered flake-food.

Rubble-zone in Lake Malawi, locality of *Pseudotropheus tropheops*

◆ *Pseudotropheus zebra*
(BOULENGER, 1899)

was not only one of the first Malawi-cichlids described scientifically, but also belongs to the Cichlids of Lake Malawi which first became obtainable for the aquarium. Due to their spectacular colour pattern, male specimens became well paid for treasures amongst European aquarists when they were first imported in the early sixties. In the meantime the species is rarely seen in pet-shops any more, the reason being the imports of a multitude of other colourful Mbuna-cichlids, and the fact that the juveniles look so drab that one can hardly imagine how splendid they will be as adults.

Males can reach a length of approximately twelve centimetres in the aquarium. As adults they are easy to distinguish from the females. Besides the bright light blue ground colouration, the distinctly enlarged ventral fins and a number of oval golden yellow spots with black borderings on the anal fin are distinctive features. Female specimens in contrast are inconspicuously greyish blue in colour.

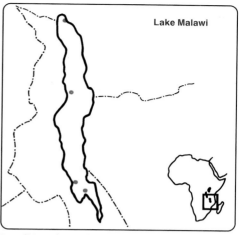

Localities of *Pseudotropheus zebra*

Pseudotropheus zebra belongs to a group of Malawi-cichlids which are characterized by a polychromatism. The description of the colouration given above refers to the most common form that entails more than ninety percent of the specimens in the natural habitat. Besides this normal morph, there are chequered specimens which are often referred to as OB-morph, being an abbreviation of Orange Blotch Morph. This

Male of the blue morph of *Pseudotropheus zebra*

variety has a light yellow to ochre ground-colouration and numerous black blotches of different shape and size. It consists almost exclusively of females whereas chequered males are extremely rare exceptions in the natural biotope. They are easily recognized by the blueish shine which becomes more distinct at times of courtship.

There are no intergrades between these two morphs. Even in crossbreeding, which is common in nature, the colour patterns of the parental specimens are passed on to the offspring in pure form.

FRYER (1959) presumed that there are two further varieties, one of which being uniformly light blue, the other pure white. Based on observations in the aquarium as well as in nature, it could be demonstrated that this is clearly an error (comp. STAECK 1972, 1978, HOLZBERG 1978, SCHRÖDER 1980). Notwithstanding that, it still appears in even very recent publications. These very popular pure white and light blue Cichlids belong to another species that was described as *Pseudotropheus callainos* STAUFFER & HERT, 1992.

The

natural habitat

of *Pseudotropheus zebra* is the rubble- and rocky littoral. Locality records have been made from the southern part as well as from the northern shore and the central west coast. I was able to also record the species from the northeastern coast (Tanzania). Whilst the normal morph hardly varies within this extensive distribution, the OB morph has developed several geographical varieties which can be identified by the arrangement, number, and shape of the black blotches. On the other hand, the males of the normal morph living in the littoral of Mumbo Island in the southwestern part of Lake Malawi have a conspicuously orange coloured dorsal fin. *P. zebra* has specialized on the lawn of algae by grating algae and micro-organisms from the boulders with the widely opened mouth pressed against the surface and closing and opening the flexible lips in quick succession.

Like in the case of most of the representatives of the genus *Pseudotropheus*, the

Female of the OB morph of *Pseudotropheus zebra*

care

is not difficult. This species should be kept in a community aquarium which is also home to other Mbuna-cichlids. Adequate co-inhabitants are other *Pseudotropheus, Labeotropheus, Melanochromis,* as well as larger robust *Nimbochromis.* Such aquarium should at least have a length of one and a half metres.

In order to provide the fish with an environment as natural as possible, it should be attempted to decorate the aquarium like a section out of the rubble- and rocky littoral. To make the fish feel home, numerous caves and other hiding-places which also divide the available floor-space into various zones, are an important prerequisite.

The usage of plants is actually not according to nature as the natural habitats of this species are bare of any higher plants. Nevertheless, some robust plants such as *Anubias nana* from West Africa, may be employed to add some patches of green to the rock-constructions.

Despite *P. zebra* being a specialized feeder on the lawn of algae, its sustenance in captivity is no problem as all common types of food are readily accepted. Food poor in fibres, like earthworms and ox-heart, should be offered only exceptionally.

If the fish are kept in a naturally decorated aquarium, no special precautions for the

breeding

need to be undertaken. *P. zebra* is an agame mouthbrooder with no bonding between the reproduction partners. This implicates that one female is not enough for a male, and a small harem is required. A stone with a horizontal smooth surface in a covered place is a preferred spawning site. The eggs are only fertilized in the mouth of the female. During the spawning act the partners circle around one another in a T-position typical for these specialized mouthbrooders. The care for the fry is an exclusive task of the mother which after spawning prefers to remain hidden or reside in calm areas of the aquarium. As the eggs with a diameter of five millimetres are rich in yolk, their development takes a long time. At a water-temperature around 27 °C the yolk sac is completely used after 19 days. The young fish need not necessarily be fed with the nauplii of *Artemia salina,* but are capable of feeding on selected small *Daphnia* and crushed flake-food or TetraOvin. If they are left in the community aquarium, the young *Pseudotropheus zebra* need not be fed separately since small food-particles left over by other fishes are sufficient to ensure their survival.

P. zebra in the rocky littoral at three metres depth

In the natural habitat of *P. zebra,* territories may be fairly small

▶ *Pseudotropheus* sp.
"acei"

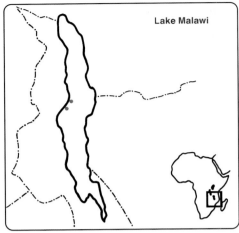

Localities of *Pseudotropheus* sp. "acei"

The first imports of this Cichlid, which still needs to be scientifically described, and is thus referred to here under its trade name, were observed in the early eighties. Because it is rarely seen in pet-shops and always comes in small numbers, it has not been widely distributed amongst aquarists.

In the aquarium, the fish reaches a length of some twelve centimetres. Its body is slender and elongate, and more or less as uniformly light blue as the head. Except for the light blue rays, the caudal fin is yellowish. The dorsal and the anal fins are blueish, but light yellow in their posterior rayed portions. The ventral fins have a smoky grey tone with a whitish margin.

The differences between the colour patterns of male and female specimens are minor; therefore sexing of juvenile and semi-adult fish is difficult. In comparison, adult females are less brilliantly coloured than males.

Male of *Pseudotropheus* sp. "acei"

The

natural habitat

of *Pseudotropheus* sp. "acei" is the transitory zone from sandy to rocky ground near the shore. The solely known localities lie on the central west coast of Lake Malawi. According to local catchers, the specimens for the pet-shop industry are caught in the area between Bandawe Point and Nkhata Bay.

Care

Keeping *Pseudotropheus* sp. "acei" creates no specific problems. Provided the fish is kept in moderately hard water with pH-values at alkaline levels, it turns out to be a robust aquarium-fish. Feeding is also easy as flake-food and all other common types of food appropriate for a Cichlid of its size are readily accepted.

The most positive results in the husbandry of *Pseudotropheus* sp. "acei" were achieved when it was not kept on its own but in a community tank in company with other Cichlids of the Mbuna-group. Such aquarium should have a minimum floor-space of 150 by 50 centimetres. Its decoration calls for coarse sand and larger stones which are piled up along the rear wall so that they form a number of den-like hiding-places. Plants may be used as additional decoration when they green the rock-constructions and not significantly limit the available swimming-space.

Breeding

Pseudotropheus sp. "acei" is an ovophile maternal mouthbrooder. No bonding develops between the reproduction partners, and two specimens only come temporarily together for the sole purpose of spawning. The eggs are taken into the mouth by the female immediately after they have been laid and fertilized there through sucking in sperm. The parental care is only performed by the female fish. The juveniles are already well developed when they leave the mouth of the mother after approximately three weeks.

Ndumbi Rocks north of Likoma Island is the locality of *Pseudotropheus* sp. "elongatus ornatus".

▶ *Pseudotropheus* sp.
"elongatus aggressive"

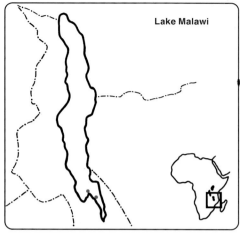

Lake Malawi

belongs to those representatives of the genus that have already been imported for the pet-shop industry in the early fifties, but which are hardly kept any more today. Male specimens may reach close to twelve centimetres in length in the aquarium; in their natural biotope they remain smaller. As males and females have distinctly different colour patterns, the identification of the sexes is an easy task. Male specimens are prettier. On a gentian-blue ground colour they show seven, blueish black transversal bands whose intensity decreases towards the tail. The head, as well as the anal and dorsal fins are mainly blueish black. The posterior portion of the anal fin carries two to three, oval, yellow spots which are bordered with black. Female specimens are greyish blue to slate-grey.

Localities of *Pseudotropheus* sp. "elongatus aggressive"

The upper rubble- and rocky littoral up to a depth of approximately twenty metres forms the

Male of *Pseudotropheus* sp. "elongatus aggressive"

natural habitat

of this species. It feeds on the lawn of algae which is either nibbled off or torn off through a quick jerk of the head. This Cichlid is exclusively found in the southwestern parts of Lake Malawi between Nkudzi and Cape Maclear as well as in the littoral of the nearby islands. Its cladistic relationship with *Pseudotropheus elongatus* FRYER, 1956, and the other representatives of the *Pseudotropheus elongatus*-group with its twenty-four members (RIBBINK et al. 1983) is still unclear.

The long-term

care

definitely requires a community aquarium. The specimens are highly unsocial amongst each other and fight and damage one another continuously if kept on their own. This also calls for large tanks of at least one and a half metres in length. Although *Pseudotropheus elongatus* belongs to the smaller Mbuna-cichlids, it is one of the most aggressive fishes in Lake Malawi. The males vehemently defend their territories and are not afraid of much bigger Cichlids. Company fishes need therefore to be robust species that can resist this fish if necessary, e.g. other *Pseudotropheus* or representatives of the genus *Melanochromis*.

A natural decoration of the tank is achieved with numerous stones and rocks which are piled up along the back wall to just under the water surface. These items simultaneously serve to divide the floor-space into several territories and also create many hiding caves of various size. The species occasionally feeds on soft leaves and shoots. Those who do not want to forgo a greening of the aquarium although there are not plants but algae in the natural biotope, should only choose hard-leaved species. *Anubias nana* and *Microsorum pteropus* have particularly proven fairly resistant in this regard. In addition, they have the advantage that they need not be planted into the substrate, but thrive well when directly attached

to the rock-constructions. The already limited swimming-space is thus not restricted any further. Feeding this Cichlid is no problem as all common types of food are readily accepted including flake-food such as TetraCichlid or TetraPhyll.

This fish is an agame mouthbrooder. Due to the fact that the males are constantly courting and ready to spawn, they require a small harem. Otherwise, their

breeding

does not require specific preparations and can take place in the community aquarium described above. The males select a spawning-site in the form of a flat stone with a smooth surface at a covered spot around which their territories extend. As in the case of all specialized mouthbrooders the eggs are taken into the mouth by the female before they are fertilized. This happens only when the female snaps at the egg dummies on the anal fin of the male and thus takes up the sperm. The oval eggs have a maximum length of five millimetres with a clutch usually containing twenty-five to thirty-five eggs. It is only the female that cares for the fry. Being rich in yolk, the larval development takes relatively long. The progress of the development processes depends greatly on the water-temperature. For example, at 23 °C the juveniles are released from the mouth of the mother fish approximately on the 23rd day, whereas at 27 °C, this happens already on the 17th day. Under the conditions of a community aquarium these periods may be extended by the fact that the mother fish feels perturbed by the other fishes and does not find a place to spit out the fry undisturbed.

As soon as the young fish have left the mouth of their mother, the maternal care soon comes to an end. The juveniles are already fairly independent and disappear in small crevices and similar sanctuaries. They measure approximately ten millimetres and feed on selected small *Daphnia* and crushed flake-food.

◆ *Pseudotropheus* sp.

"elongatus Mpanga"

This scientifically undescribed species was discovered by ornamental fish catchers relatively late. It obviously belongs to the group of less elongate Cichlids in the *Pseudotropheus elongatus* species-complex which holds, according to RIBBINK and co-authors (1983), altogether 24 species. As no valid species name is available at this stage, the fish are temporarily named after their collecting site here.

Due to the fact that the locality in the far north of the western shore of Lake Malawi where this Cichlid occurs is fairly difficult to access, it has only been imported on rare occasions and in small numbers. The species belongs to the smaller representatives of the genus *Pseudotropheus* with a maximum total length of just under ten centimetres. Most of the imported specimens measure approximately seven centimetres.

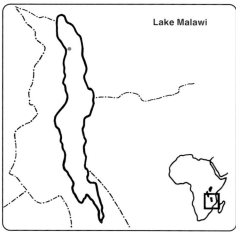

Locality of *Pseudotropheus* sp. "elongatus Mpanga"

Courting males display a bright, light blue background colouration with the flanks being marked with seven black transversal bands whose intensity gradually

Male of *Pseudotropheus* sp. "elongatus Mpanga"

diminishes from the front to the rear. Two further such stripes run over the nape and forehead region. The lower portion of the head, the throat, and the ventral fins are also black whilst the dorsal and anal fins have broad black submarginal bands. The anal fin may have up to five light yellow egg dummies. The posterior portion of the dorsal fin and the caudal fin are mainly yellow with the latter being bordered with broad black submarginal bands on the top and bottom edges.

Unfortunately, only dominant courting males display this attractive colour pattern. Suppressed male specimens merely resemble females and are inconspicuously greyish blue to greyish black with an indistinct pattern of black transversal bands.

The

natural habitat

of this species of *Pseudotropheus* is confined to the northwestern part of the coast of Lake Malawi. Localities are only known from the vicinity of the village of Chilumba where the fish lives in the littoral of the off-shore islands, e.g. Chirwa Island and Mpanga Rocks. Showing a tight bonding to rock crevices and caves, this Cichlid preferably inhabits the upper rocky littoral at depths between three and five metres. A very similarly coloured Cichlid occurs on the small Masimbwe Island in the south of Likoma.

Care

The fish is unproblematic and is best kept in a larger aquarium that emulates a section of the rocky littoral and also accommodates other Mbuna-cichlids. It is recommendable to keep one male together with two or three females. Under these conditions the

breeding

is fairly easy. This Cichlid belongs to the specialized mouthbrooders where the female takes care of the clutch all on her own. After an incubation period of approximately three weeks the already very independent juveniles are released from the mouth.

P. sp. "yellow tail" from Masimbwe Island closely resembles *P.* sp. "elongatus Mpanga".

◗ *Pseudotropheus* sp.
"elongatus ornatus"

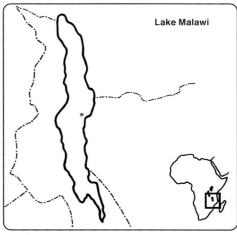

Lake Malawi

Locality of *P.* sp. "elongatus ornatus"

is another species without a name, i.e that has not yet been scientifically described. Due to the fact that body shape and colour pattern slightly resemble *Pseudotropheus elongatus,* aquarists refer to this fish under its trade name *Pseudotropheus* "ornatus".

Male specimens of this species may reach a body length of approximately eleven centimetres. With a distinct sexual dichromatism being present, the identification of the sexes of adult fish is easy. On a light blue to turquoise ground colour, the males have a pattern of six to seven blueish black transversal bands extending over the flanks. These bands decrease in intensity poste-

Pseudotropheus sp. "elongatus ornatus" in its natural biotope at four metres depth

riorly. Females have the same banded pattern, but an olive to yellowish grey ground colouration. Their dorsal and anal fins have a conspicuously broad blueish black marginal stripe.

The
natural habitat
of this Cichlid is the rocky littoral. Its distribution appears to be unusually restricted with the only localities known being Makulawe Point and Ndumbi Rocks north of the island of Likoma. This area, not larger than a soccer field consists of an underwater reef that maximally extends up to two metres below the surface. This reef has a surprisingly dense population of Cichlids. The most common species with whom this species shares its habitat are *Cynotilapia afra* and an undescribed Cichlid which resembles *Melanochromis parallelus*. Due to the extraordinary population density in this biotope, all Mbuna-cichlids appear to be feeding less on the lawn of algae but more on the plankton that is supplied by the strong currents above the reef.

Care

Keeping this species is not difficult. A aquaria of at least one metre in length are adequate. Like all other Mbuna-cichlids it is best kept in a naturally decorated community tank. In comparison with other representatives of this genus, the species appears to be less aggressive towards other fishes. Even amongst themselves they are comparatively tolerant. Nonetheless one should not keep them in pairs, but a male should have two or three females.

When decorating the aquarium it should be borne in mind that the fish only feels at ease when there is a sufficient number of crevices and alcoves that may be used as sanctuaries. Being plant-tolerant, robust plants may be utilized as additional decoration items. They should not be planted too densely because, as the photograph of the biotope shows, plants are actually alien to the natural habitat. In no case should they limit the available space for swimming.

Since the fish accepts the commonly used types of food, their feeding does not cause any problems. A varying diet is given when *Daphnia* and insect larvae are offered besides flake-food, e.g. TetraMin, Tetra-Cichlid, or TetraPhyll.

The
breeding
should preferably take place in the community aquarium from which, if necessary, the female is removed a short time before the development of the juveniles is completed. At water-temperatures around 27 °C this is due after nearly three weeks. Like the other Mbuna-cichlids this species is an agame mouthbrooder where the female alone cares for the clutch. When leaving the mouth of their mother, the juveniles are already capable of feeding on tiny *Daphnia* and crushed flake-food.

When properly made up, aquarium fishes may become a good meal.

▶ *Pseudotropheus* sp.
"zebra Chilumba"

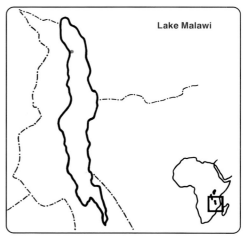

Locality of *Pseudotropheus* sp. "zebra Chilumba"

As with regard to body shape and colouration, this Cichlid shows a close resemblance with *Pseudotropheus zebra* (BOULENGER, 1899). Due to this reason RIBBINK and co-authors (1983) included it in *Pseudotropheus zebra* species-complex which altogether consolidates 27 forms. One of the features that allow distinction from other members of this cladistic group is the broad black submarginal band which extends over almost the entire length of the dorsal fin and which is especially conspicuous in fully grown males.

Under aquarium conditions, the fish may reach approximately twelve centimetres in length. A distinct sexual dichromatism makes the identification of the sexes easy. The males are bright light blue to turquoise in colour. Seven black transversal bands mark the flanks; their intensity gradually decreases from the front to the rear end. The anterior ones extend onto the dorsal fin which additionally has a broad black submarginal longitudinal band. The anal fin of

Male of *Pseudotropheus* sp. "zebra Chilumba"

male specimens has three to five yellow oval spots which are bordered black. Except for the anterior edges, the ventral fin is black. The throat region and the gill-skins are usually yellow.

This description of the colour and pattern applies to a morph found in the immediate vicinity of the village of Chilumba and on the Chitande Islands farther to the north. But there are other colour varieties, e.g. those with white throat instead of a yellow one on Mpanga Rocks. More to the south, near Usisya and Mpandi Point, the males have a deep yellow section in the posterior dorsal fin. Females from all localities have an inconspicuous greyish blue to blackish grey background colouration with the banded pattern usually being relatively faint.

Unfortunately this exceptionally attractive Cichlid is only very rarely imported since its collecting sites are relatively difficult to reach.

The
natural habitat

of *Pseudotropheus* sp. "zebra Chilumba" is strictly confined to the northwestern coast of Lake Malawi. The only known localities lie between Mpandi Point or Usisya in the south and the Chitande Islands in the north. In this area the fish inhabit the rubble- and rocky littoral, but they are also frequently encountered in transitory zone to sandy areas. The preferred depth approximately lies between two and fifteen metres. RIBBINK and co-authors (1983) even observed this species at depths below twenty metres. Due to its bright colouration and commonness, this species can immediately be spotted in biotopes where it occurs.

The most important source of food for this fish certainly is the algal felt that covers stones and rocks in the upper shore zone. At times of rich plankton development this source is also utilized.

Pseudotropheus sp. "zebra Chilumba" in its natural habitat (Chirwa Island near Chilumba)

◆ *Pseudotropheus* sp.
"zebra tangerine"

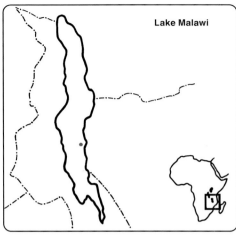

Lake Malawi

This pretty Cichlid caused disbelieving surprise amongst aquarists when it was first imported. Despite its bright and striking colours, its morphometric data closely resemble *Pseudotropheus zebra*. Yet, it is not just another colour morph of this species, but a distinct species. Due to the fact that its scientific description is still outstanding, no name is available that would allow to refer to this fish properly.

Together with three or four other undescribed species, this Cichlid forms a group of fishes which all closely resemble *Pseudotropheus zebra* and which are therefore temporarily and indefinitely assigned to the *Pseudotropheus zebra*-complex. The opinion that the Cichlid portrayed here is a separate species is supported by the observation that this fish does not generally mate with other species of the *zebra*-complex.

Locality of *Pseudotropheus* sp. "zebra tangerine"

Purposely induced cross-breeds showed that the offspring always had a mixed pattern of elements derived from the colour patterns of both the parental forms. Inter-

Pseudotropheus sp. "zebra tangerine", male of the blue morph

162

mediate forms like this are unknown from the natural habitats of these fishes.

The peculiar feature that should be pointed out here because it allows to distinguish it from other Cichlids of the *zebra*-complex, is the unusual high number of egg dummies on the anal fin of fully grown males. As can be seen in the photograph, the fin is marked with more than a dozen of these yellow spots which are bordered with black.

It is furthermore remarkable that this fish is polymorph, i.e. there are not less than three different colour morphs. The normal variety, i.e. the one most commonly found in the natural habitat, is blue. Mature males are mainly light blue whereas the more inconspicuous females are blueish grey.

The most popular morph amongst aquarists is the orange coloured variety which almost exclusively consists of females. In the natural biotopes, male of this morph are extremely rare. Up to a length of approxi-

mately six centimetres they have the colour pattern of the females, but on reaching maturity they gradually become lighter. Adult specimens eventually display reddish beige to light rosy colours which assumes a distinct blue underlay during periods of courtship.

By means of select breeding, it was achieved to considerably increase the number of males of the orange morph in the aquarium population. There are also breeding stocks where the males can be identified already when juvenile due to their lighter colouration.

The third morph of this Cichlid, the so-called OB morph, also consists almost exclusively of females. On a yellowish orange ground colour they have an irregular pattern of small and large black spots and speckles all over the body and the fins. The extremely rare males of this morph look like females until reaching maturity when they assume a blueish underlay. In courting

Pseudotropheus sp. "zebra tangerine", male of the orange morph

specimens the markings may fade to such an extent that they may sometimes appear almost uniformly light blue.

The
natural habitat
of this fish which reaches approximately twelve centimetres in the aquarium is the rubble- and rocky littoral. As far as is known to date, the distribution is restricted to a very small area on the east coast of Lake Malawi. According to the discoverers and catchers the only known locality lies in the vicinity of the village of Metangula in Mozambique.

Since the prohibition of all exports of ornamental fish from Mozambique, wild-caught specimens have not been imported into Europe or America any more.

Care

Keeping this fish calls for an aquarium of approximately one and a half metres in length. Its decoration should emulate the rubble- and rocky littoral as closely as possible. A male should be given two or three females. Most positive experiences with this Cichlid were made in a community aquarium where it was in the company of other Malawi-cichlids, e.g. representatives of the genera *Labeotropheus, Melano-chromis,* and *Pseudotropheus.*

Attention must be paid to the diet of this fish. Although it feeds on all commonly used types of food like the other Mbuna-cichlids, an inadequate diet will soon lead to the intense orange colouration fading and becoming an unattractive tone of ivory. An important precondition for the maintenance of the natural colouration is the supply of carotenes. Therefore, small species of shrimp should be given regularly. If by any means possible, juveniles should initially be fed exclusively on *Cyclops.* Flake-food with a content of this pigment, e.g. TetraRubin, is also recommendable.

The
breeding
takes preferably place in a community aqua-rium as described above. If the juveniles can find a sufficient number of small cavities and crevices, a few of them will survive even in the company of predatory fishes in the same tank.

If it is intended to rear the fry without losses, it is advisable to transfer the female from the community aquarium to a separate breeding tank where it may care for the fry undisturbed.

When breeding with this species it is important to know that every fry of any given female may contain specimens of all three morphs. Since there are no intermedi-ate or mixed forms, it is insignificant which colour morph is selected to breed with.

If males and females belong to the same colour variety, a particularly large percent-age of juveniles will obviously have the col-ours shown by the parents. Twenty to forty juveniles may be expected per spawning. They can easily be reared on nauplii of the Brine Shrimp.

The various colour morphs of *Pseudotropheus* sp. "zebra tangerine" can already be distinguished when the juveniles leave the mouth of the mother.

164

The Genus

Spathodus

was established by BOULENGER as early as in 1901. Its distribution is restricted to Lake Tanganyika and it consolidates the two species *Spathodus erythrodon* and *Spathodus marlieri*. Together with representatives of the monotypic genera *Eretmodus* and *Tanganicodus*, they form a group of four closely resembling species which are distinctly different from all other Tanganyika-cichlids.

The shared features of these four Cichlids include morphology, ecological requirements, and behaviourial biology. On the other hand, it is remarkable that they differ considerably in their parental care behaviour. Whilst some care for the fry in a mother-family, there are others where the female as well as the male participate in the parental care so that one may talk about a biparent family in these cases.

Accounting for their many shared features, these four species are commonly consolidated under the term Goby Cichlids. The reason for this name is the ecology of these fishes in their natural habitats. Similar to some Gobies of subtropical or tropical oceans, they preferably reside in the shallow water of rocky coastal zones in which they dash around more leaping than swimming.

▶ Spathodus erythrodon
BOULENGER, 1901

is a small Cichlid with a maximum length of eight centimetres. The fish is monomorphous, i.e. males and females show no clearly defined differences in their appearance. Therefore, the definite identification of the sexes on external characters is impossible. To a certain extent, the fins may be of help. They may be larger in the male. In particular, their ventral fins are longer

Spathodus erythrodon

than in the females. They may also grow slightly larger.

The ground colour of the fish depends on the colour of the substrate and may vary between khaki grey, greenish brown, and brownish beige. The flanks are marked with some radiant turquoise spots which appear to be arranged in three or four longitudinal rows. The same tone of colour is also found on the lips. The presence of these shining spots depends on the prevailing mood and whether the specimen feels at ease. In an unsuitable environment these markings may completely vanish.

The

natural habitat

of this Goby Cichlid is the shallow water zone of the rubble-littoral. The preferred depth of water lies between thirty and fifty centimetres, and the fish was never observed below one metre. The presently known localities are on the southwestern shore (Zaïre) and on the northern coast (Burundi, Tanzania). Although the fish thus supposedly has a wide distribution, it is not encountered everywhere where there are suitable biotopes. In the lake, they exist in several isolated populations and have an awkwardly disjunct distribution. Observations in the natural habitat and in captivity showed that this fish sustains itself exclusively on the lawn of algae.

Care

Keeping Goby Cichlids is generally very easy since their natural environment can be emulated in the aquarium without great effort. To appropriately house the species, aquaria of at least one metre in length are necessary.

Light sand or very fine gravel should be used for the ground. The decoration is made up of fist-sized stones that are arranged in such a way that a rubble-field is emulated which provides numerous crevices and cavities of various sizes. A multitude of very

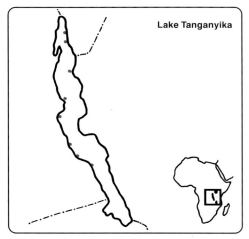

Localities of *Spathodus erythrodon*

small grottos is particularly important since these later serve the juveniles as safe sanctuaries. Although plants are in contradiction to the natural habitat, the aquarium may nevertheless be greened as this Cichlid even leaves the most delicate offshoots untouched. It is recommendable to limit the number of plants to such an extent that they do not obstruct the available ground- and free swimming-space.

As a fairly firm bonding develops between the reproduction partners, *Spathodus erythrodon* is preferably kept in pairs. Whilst an aquarium of one metre in length cannot accommodate more than one pair, larger tanks may obviously be home to two or even three pairs. The fish does well in a community aquarium which also houses other Tanganyika-cichlids from the upper rubble-littoral. Adequate choices can be made from the smaller species of *Julidochromis*, *Telmatochromis*, and *Neolamprologus*, but also *Tropheus*. *Spathodus* is tolerant and unaggressive towards these Cichlids.

Feeding this species is no problem as all commonly used types of food are willingly accepted. In order to guarantee a diet as varying as possible, *Daphnia*, White Mosquito larvae, and the various types of flake-food are offered alternatingly.

The

breeding

should preferably take place in the community aquarium described above. Provided with adequate space and a healthy diet, the fish breeds relatively easily thus it is surprising that breeding records are so few and far between. The reason most likely is an inadequate environment.

On some occasions specimens of the same sex were kept together instead of a pair, or the supposed breeding partners even belonged to different species. Unfortunately it is common practice that the fishes are mixed up in the tanks of the pet shops and difficult to distinguish.

Spathodus erythrodon is a mouthbrooder, but displays a caring behaviour that is highly unusual for this ethological group. Already a few days before spawning takes place, male and female can be observed together patrolling their territory.

A smooth stone is usually chosen as spawning site whereby a very oblique, almost vertical surface is often preferred to a horizontal one.

During the spawning act the fish circle around one another in the T-position typical for mouthbrooders. The female takes one or, more seldom, two eggs into the mouth immediately after they have been released. By sucking in the male's sperm they are then fertilized inside the mouth.

In contrast to the majority of mouthbrooders, the bonding between the partners is continued after the spawning. At a water-temperature around 27 °C the female carries the eggs and subsequent larvae for approximately twelve days. Displaying a very characteristic advertising and transfer behaviour, it eventually passes the larvae on to the male which then cares for the fry for about another week more.

Observations made under aquarium conditions indicate that if disturbing factors prevent this obviously normal transfer, the female is also able to complete the mouthbrooding care all on her own.

It is only in exceptional cases that a clutch contains more than twenty eggs. Once the juveniles have been spat out, the parental fish apparently does not take them back into the mouth again. It is therefore crucial that the young fish have crevices and caves available into which they may retreat immediately in order to avoid potentially predatory fishes.

If bred in a community tank, the minute size of the juveniles may become a problem. Although they already measure approximately ten millimetres in length when they leave the mouth, they are only two millimetres high, i.e. they are very slender and elongate. Without a rubble-field with its ample hiding places being present, they soon fall prey to other fishes even when the company fishes in the aquarium belong to species that do usually not feed on young fishes.

Other than that, it can only be recommended to rear the fry in a separate tank when the specimens can be transferred into a completely decorated clean aquarium. Since the juveniles permanently lie on the ground, they are very sensitive towards decay, leftovers of food, and similar substances. If cleanliness is not given the highest priority, losses will constantly be experienced.

Further problems arise from the tininess of the juveniles when it comes to their feeding. It is obvious that they are only capable of swallowing microscopic prey-items. In the beginning, newly hatched nauplii of *Artemia salina*, the Brine Shrimp, are the only choice. Finely grated flake-food may also be accepted, but only as long as it still floats in the water and has not yet sunk to the ground.

Their feeding is furthermore a problem because they stay close to their hiding-cave and do not swim around to search for food. This results in the necessity to make respective hiding-places available all over the floor-space and also have a powerful filtration system creating so strong a current that the food cannot sink to the ground.

167

The Genus

Tanganicodus

was suggested by POLL in 1950. It is endemic to Lake Tanganyika and is monotypic, i.e. incorporates only one species. Like the representatives of the preceding genus, this fish is also referred to as a Goby Cichlid.

The typical feature which enables its distinction from other species and which is also recognizable in live specimens is the clearly low-set mouth. It is much smaller and narrower than in the cases of the three other Goby Cichlids.

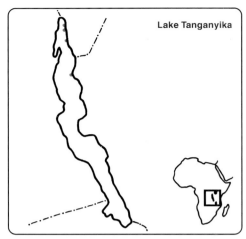

Localities of *Tanganicodus irsacae*

◗ *Tanganicodus irsacae*
POLL, 1950

reaches a maximum body length of just seven centimetres and is therefore rightfully described as a Dwarf Cichlid. Since there are only minor morphological differences between the males and the females, the identification of the sexes is extremely difficult; older male specimens may have slightly enlarged ventral fins. Depending on the col-

our of the ground, the fish may be khaki-grey to greenish brown. A pattern of seven ochre to ivory coloured transversal bands is confined to the lower half of the body. The head and anterior portion of the upper body are marked with light green, glossy metallic blotches. A larger, indefinitely bordered, dark blotch is found in the central part of the dorsal fin.

Tanganicodus irsacae

The

natural habitat

of this Cichlid is the shallow water of the rubble-zone. It appears that the fish hardly ever proceed to depths greater than one metre. All localities know to date lie in the northern half of Lake Tanganyika including the western shore (Zaïre) as well as the eastern coast (Burundi, Tanzania). The fish sustains itself on the algal felt that covers the surface of the rocks lying in the water. They feed on the algae themselves and on microorganisms living amongst them. POLL reported that examinations of the stomach contents revealed that this Cichlid preys upon insect larvae and crustaceans besides filamentous algae and infusoria.

Its care

is appropriate in a naturally decorated community aquarium of at least one metre in length. Since its ecological requirements are largely identical to those described for the preceding species, reference is made to the information supplied there.

When it comes to feeding *Tanganicodus irsacae*, it should be borne in mind that the fish has a very small mouth. A suitably varying diet is achieved when *Daphnia*, Mosquito larvae, and a variety of flake-foods are offered.

Only a few reports exist about the

breeding

of this Cichlid, the reason being probably that it is so rarely imported. It belongs to the small group of biparental mouthbrooders where both the female and the male participate in hatching the juveniles. The female fish takes the spawn into her mouth and passes on the larvae to the male after a few days. The latter then completes the parental care.

Freshly caught Tanganyika-cichlids are transported to the storing tanks.

The Genus

Telmatochromis

was described by BOULENGER as early as 1898. At present, it accommodates five species whose distribution is restricted to Lake Tanganyika. It is to be expected that a few more species will be described in the near future. Some of these have already made their debuts in the ornamental fish trade.

◗ *Telmatochromis vittatus*
BOULENGER, 1898

may reach a maximum body size of approximately nine centimetres. The fish is monomorphous, i.e. there are no definite external features that would differentiate males and females. Thus, the identification of the sexes of live specimens is extremely difficult. To a certain extent, the fins may give hints — they are slightly larger in adult

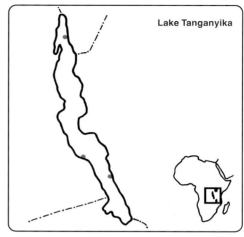

Localities of *Telmatochromis vittatus*

male individuals. The ventral fins in particular appear to be more produced in males than in females.

In both sexes the upper half of the body is brownish grey whilst the lower half is ivory coloured. A dark longitudinal band ranges from the angle of the mouth through the eye

Telmatochromis vittatus

and over the flanks up to the base of the caudal fin. Another black longitudinal stripe runs along the base of the dorsal fin. The caudal peduncle is marked with an indistinct dark splodge.

The

natural habitat

of this species is the shallow coastal zone of the rubble- and rocky littoral. Localities are known from the southwest (Zaïre) as well as from the southeast (Tanzania) and the northeast (Burundi). Although the fish thus has a wide distribution in Lake Tanganyika, it is not really common.

With the prerequisite of a harmonizing pair, the

care

may take place in a relatively small aquarium of approximately fifty centimetres. It is nevertheless more advisable to keep it in a community tank of more than one metre in length because it offers by far more opportunities for interesting observations. The decoration of the aquarium should in either case emulate the natural environment. Stones and small boulders should be arranged in such a way that cavities of different sizes are created. These rock constructions may be piled up on the back wall of the tank up to just under the water surface. *T. vittatus* is plant-tolerant, but a dense vegetation would be inadequate and not according to the natural biotope.

Co-inhabitants of the community tank may be chosen from the species of Goby Cichlids, *Julidochromis*, *Chalinochromis*, and *Neolamprologus*. The diet should consist of *Daphnia*, insect larvae, and a variety of flake-foods.

For the purpose of

breeding

it is recommendable to transfer the pair to a separate aquarium. Since this Cichlid be-

longs to the cave brooders, a natural decoration with appropriate cavities and crevices is of particular importance. The eggs, larvae, and juveniles are cared for by both male and female in a parental family-structure.

The juveniles are still relatively small when they appear in front of the breeding-den for the first time. They definitely require freshly hatched nauplii of the Brine Shrimp, *Artemia salina,* and finely grated flake-food or TetraOvin. In contrast to the cave brooders of West Africa dealt with in Volume 1, they do not conglomerate in a school which is guided through the aquarium by the parents. The young *Telmatochromis* are more attached to the immediate vicinity of their breeding-cave in the centre of a territory defended by both the parents.

Spiny eel in the rubble-zone of Lake Tanganyika

171

Amongst the multitude of Cichlids described from Lake Tanganyika there are many which are very popular aquarium fishes. However, it appears to be a fact that the Cichlid enthusiasts have always been favouring

the genus Tropheus

in particular. This is the more astounding as its representatives are by no means appropriate fishes for the beginner. They all have an extremely high degree of intraspecific aggression, are relatively susceptible to infectional diseases of the digestive tract, and can soon become a great disappointment when not properly kept. In addition to the aforesaid, these fishes are usually fairly expensive. Possibly it is just all this that attracts some aquarists to acquire these Cichlids.

On the other hand, there are also a couple of pros that make the husbandry of these Cichlids attractive. Some *Tropheus* populations may have a particularly conspicuous and contrasting colour pattern. Moreover, the highly specialized mouthbrooding behaviour of the females promises observations as interesting as the differentiated aggressive behaviour of all representatives of this systematic unit.

The genus, endemic to Lake Tanganyika, was described by BOULENGER as early as in 1898. Today, it incorporates six species, not all of which are sufficiently diagnosed and properly distinguished from other members of the genus. A detailed revision of this systematic unit therefore appears to be urgently needed. Based upon numerous diagnostic features, including ecological and behaviourial ones, the stati of the four species *Tropheus duboisi* MARLIER, 1959, *T. polli* AXELROD, 1977, *T. annectens* BOULENGER, 1900 (comp. BRICHARD 1989), and *T. moorii* BOULENGER, 1898, are commonly accepted. The differentiation of *Tropheus brichardi* NELISSEN & THYS, 1975, and *T. kasabae* Nelissen, 1977, on the other hand, is less well founded, and the specific rank of the latter in particular is questionable.

In recent times, it was repeatedly undertaken to consolidate the approximately 50 presently known populations in groups or to assign them to certain species (a. o. BRICHARD 1989, KONINGS 1988). All these attempts were more of hypothetic character, partially based upon questionable criteria and methods, and do not stand a serious examination.

Interesting and new data on the cladistic relationships between various species and populations of *Tropheus* and their evolution resulted from the comparative studies of their genetics (STURMBAUER & MEYER 1992). According to this, certain forms have a greater genetic resemblance to populations on the opposite side of the lake than to immediately adjacent populations.

Sandy beach in the vicinity of Kigoma

The first description of

◗ *Tropheus brichardi*
NELISSEN & THYS, 1975

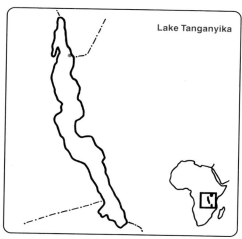

Locality of *Tropheus brichardi*

was already published by MATTHES in 1962 who followed MARLIER (1959) and considered this Cichlid to be a geographical colour morph of *Tropheus moorii*. Amongst aquarists, this fish has become popular under the name "Chocolate-*moorii*".

It reaches a body length of approximately twelve centimetres. With a sexual dimorphism absent, a definite identification of the sexes based upon external characteristics is impossible. To a certain extent, the sex may be assumed from the shape of the fins. Especially the ventral fins are longer in older males than in females. Relatively reliable results can be gained from an examination of the genital papilla with a magnifying glass.

Fully grown specimens appear to be almost unicoloured mustard-brown. In the upper half of the body there is an elongate lemon- to zinc-yellow blotch which usually extends from the fourth and the eleventh ray of the dorsal fin to the lateral line. In some specimens it may even further continue onto the base of the dorsal fin. The same shade of yellow is also found on the lower part of the body in the region of the belly. The iris is white with a yellow upper edge. The mouth is surrounded by a blackish zone. In contrast, juveniles have a yellowish striped pattern which gradually disappears when the fish reach maturity.

Tropheus brichardi

173

The
natural habitat
of this Cichlid is the upper region of the rubble- and rocky littoral near the shore. It is only in exceptional cases that it is encountered a greater depths than some ten metres. Its preferred depth lies between two and five metres.

The fish inhabits a fairly small area and its distribution is limited to the south of Burundi near the Tanzanian border. A confirmed locality is Nyanza Lac. This Cichlid has specialized on the algal lawn that covers the stones and boulders of the shore zone. It feeds on the algae and the microorganisms living in between.

Care

Keeping this Cichlid definitely requires a very spacious aquarium of at least one and a half metres in length. The reason for this is the high intraspecific aggression of this fish. Even in extra large tanks it will therefore be impossible in the long run to keep two adult males together.

The best husbandry results can be achieved when one male is kept together with half a dozen or more females. In groups smaller than this, one runs the risk that the aggressive actions of the dominant specimens focuses on individual members of the group which ultimately leads to their untimely death. The killing of conspecifics is a result of the unnatural living conditions in the aquarium, i.e. the limited available space that does not allow the inferior specimen to avoid the territory of the dominant fish. A good chance to build up a harmonizing group exists when a number of juveniles can grow up together in a tank.

The naturally decorated aquarium emulates a section of the rubble or rocky littoral. Not only is it important that stones and small boulders are used to create as many cavities as possible, but that these also serve as visual screens that separate individual territories.

A dense vegetation in an aquarium for these Cichlids is absolutely inadequate. For one it is in contradiction to the natural biotope, for the other it narrows the available swimming-space for these active and swift swimmers to an unacceptable extent.

It is not at all necessary to keep these Cichlids on their own. Although they like to fight with each other, they are surprisingly tolerant towards other species. However, calmer and less fast fishes, such as the majority of the species of *Neolamprologus*, do not make appropriate co-inhabitants of a *Tropheus* aquarium. Instead, positive results were achieved with Goby Cichlids and species of *Julidochromis*.

Feeding this food specialist is not a problem if the various types of flake-food, e.g. TetraMin and TetraPhyll, *Daphnia,* and White Mosquito larvae are offered alternatingly. Ox-heart, earthworms and similar types of food poor in fibres appear less suitable for this species.

The
breeding
in the naturally decorated aquarium described above does not require any special preparations. If appropriate attention was paid to the availability of small crevices and cavities in which the juveniles may retreat during their first days and weeks, the fry of small *Tropheus* will also grow up without losses when other Cichlids are present in the tank.

Tropheus brichardi is an agame mouthbrooder which cares for its offspring in a mother-family. At a water temperature of approximately 27 °C it takes about four weeks until the juveniles leave the mouth of the mother for the first time. It is important that the female is regularly fed during this period of mouthbrooding care.

◗ *Tropheus duboisi*
MARLIER, 1959

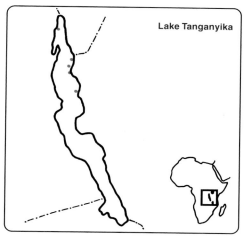

Lake Tanganyika

Localities of *Tropheus duboisi*

was imported alive into Germany even before its scientific description, i.e. in 1958. However, it subsequently disappeared again. The next imports were not observed before 1974, after it was almost simultaneously discovered by several parties, amongst others by the author. The species does not only occur in Zaïre, but also in the vicinity of Kigoma in Tanzania.

The fish may reach a size of approximately thirteen centimetres. With a sexual dimorphism absent, males and females can hardly be distinguished upon external features when alive. To a certain extent, the length of the ventral fin may provide an answer as these are usually filamentous in older males. Adult specimens have a light transversal band over the flanks whose colour varies with the place of origin. It may be pearl-white or sulphur-yellow in its upper portion. The width of this body-belt may also vary; whilst it may only be two to three scales broad in some specimens, it may cover six scales or fifteen millimetres in breadth in those from certain other localities. In adult specimens, the entire head has a brilliant blue colouration.

A feature particular to this species is that it passes through an extreme cycle of

Tropheus duboisi busy spawning

colour changes during the process of ageing. The very attractive juvenile pattern has not the least resemblance to that of the adult fish. When leaving the mouth of the mother, the pitch black background colouration is speckled with a multitude of bright white dots that are scattered over the head, body, and the fins. These appear to be grouped in seven or eight vertical and four to five horizontal bands on the flanks. With increasing age, the number of dots gradually decreases from the base of the tail to the head. On reaching six to seven centimetres after approximately one year, they have vanished completely. It is noteworthy that females retain this spotted pattern for a longer period than their male siblings.

The

natural habitat

of this Cichlid is the deeper and lower zone of the rocky littoral. Since the adult individuals generally reside at depths between three and fifteen metres, their preferred levels clearly lie below those inhabited by *Tropheus moorii*. Only the juveniles of *T. duboisi* live in the shallow water of the rubble-zone near the shore until they reach a size of approximately six centimetres. Another difference to *T. moorii* is that *T. duboisi* is never encountered in groups or schools which is the rule in the former species. It is more of an individualist. Therefore it is only on rare occasions that the scuba-diver is able to observe two specimens at the same time.

The disjunct distribution of this species in Lake Tanganyika is fairly remarkable. The first known locality was a small area in the vicinity of the village of Bemba in the north-western corner of the lake in Zaïre. The species is absent from Burundian territory. Fifteen years after the discovery of the species it was established that it also inhabits another, fairly large area in the north of Tanzania. With gaps in between, it extends from the border of Burundi through to the vicinity of Kigoma up to south of the mouth of the Malagarasi. This region is inhabited by two geographical colour morphs which differ with regard to the hue and the breadth of the transversal band. Particularly pretty specimens with a broad yellow body belt are found south of the mouth of the Lugufu River.

Semi-adult *T. duboisi* inhabit the rubble-zone (Kigoma, two metres deep) where they are safe from pursuit.

Although the eight day old juveniles of *T. duboisi* are already fairly large, the mother still takes them into her mouth.

Care

In the long run, the successful maintenance of adult specimens of *Tropheus duboisi* will only be possible if very large aquaria are available. This fish is a typical representative of the genus *Tropheus* in so far that it can show a high degree of intraspecific aggression. However, in comparison with *Tropheus moorii* they still appear more social. A male is preferably kept together with two or three females. A firm ranking is soon established in this group. When threatened by a higher ranking specimen, the inferior displays a trembling that serves as a calming gesture of humility. The same behaviour is also shown by the male during courtship, with the difference being that it is more spontaneous and is followed by guiding in most of the cases.

The decoration of the aquarium calls for stones and small boulders which are arranged in such a manner that crevices and caves of different size are created. Simultaneously, these should serve as visual screens that simplify the definition of territorial borders. Since there are no aquatic plants in the natural biotope except for algae, planting the aquarium is inadequate. If done so, one should choose plants which anchor on the rock constructions, e.g. *Anubias nana* or *Microsorum pteropus*. These do not limit the available floor- and swimming-space.

Tropheus duboisi should also be kept in a community aquarium since the intraspecific aggression becomes less disturbing in the presence of other fishes. *Tropheus moorii*, the Goby Cichlids, and *Julidochromis* have proven to be appropriate for this purpose. The diet should preferably consist of flake-food, *Daphnia*, and White Mosquito larvae.

Provided with a varying menu and a naturally decorated aquarium, the

breeding

will take place more or less spontaneously. The breeding partners come only together for the sole purpose of spawning. Courtship is short and fairly primitive in comparison with substratum-brooders. The only behavioural trait that could be regarded as signal from the female for its readiness to spawn, is when it follows the guiding male. A more or less horizontal stone-plate which is covered above by overhanging rocks is a preferred spawning site.

Courtship and spawning acts resemble the typical reproductive behaviour of *Pseudotropheus* and other Haplochomines to the full. The breeding partners slowly circle around one another on a circular orbit and assume a T-position. This means whilst one fish releases its sexual products, the other one follows it with the mouth close to the urogenital papilla. The female releases the eggs one by one, in exceptional cases two at a time. Immediately after one egg has been laid she takes it into the mouth. It is only there that the eggs come into contact with the sperm.

A clutch is extremely small, and hardly ever results in more than ten juveniles. Observations made under aquarium conditions showed that many more eggs are frequently laid, but their number is reduced during the mouthbrooding care of the female to an extent that is obviously the maximum. Amongst approximately twenty females examined by the author in Lake Tanganyika, none carried more than ten larvae.

The elongate eggs rich in yolk have a maximum length of seven millimetres and are thus unusually large. Since the speed of the larval development depends on the amount of yolk available, the species of *Tropheus* have the longest development period of all Cichlids. In the case of *T. duboisi* it takes approximately thirty days at 27°C until the mother releases the juveniles from her mouth for the first time.

This data refers to a specimen kept on its own. In the community aquarium, the female may keep the fry even longer when it feels disturbed. For the breeder it is important to know that, in contrast to other mouthbrooders, the females of *T. duboisi* regularly feed during the brooding period beginning on the day when spawning takes place. Nevertheless, it is astounding that the caring female is even able to prey upon White Mosquito larvae.

Moreover, it is also surprising that the juveniles already begin to feed whilst still in the mouth of the mother. Test specimens which had been removed from the mouth of the female and confirmedly had not been outside before, defecated immediately afterwards.

When leaving the mouth of the mother, the juveniles already measure between twelve and fifteen millimetres which indicates that different breeds may have different sizes. It is to be presumed that the amount of yolk depends on the nutritional condition of the female. Although the young fish are already fairly independent, the mother usually continues with her intense care for another eight to ten days. In the beginning, the slightest disturbance initiates her to take the fry back into the mouth.

During the early stages, the juveniles will still spend a lot of time in the mouth, later they only sleep there. Due to their considerable size they are capable of feeding on White Mosquito larvae and other large prey-items right from the beginning on and grow extremely fast. After one week they are already so big that not all of them find place in the mouth of the mother. Only a few of them can then spend the night hours there.

Due to the permanent feeding during the caring period, the females are ready for the next spawning already three weeks later.

Once the mouthbrooding care of the female has ceased, the young fish seeks cover in a rock crevice which becomes the centre of a territory that is defended against other juveniles.

▶ *Tropheus moorii*
BOULENGER, 1898

The first specimens of this species reached Europe towards the end of the previous century. They were amongst a larger number of fishes collected for the British Museum by the Englishman MOORE in Lake Tanganyika during years 1895 and 1896. What the ichthyologist BOULENGER had before him to be the basis for his original description of the species, was preserved material. Therefore, his description of the colouration does not give an impression of how it looks alive. As is commonly known, preserved specimens very soon lose or change their colours. As MOORE had collected his fishes in the vicinity of the village Kinyamkolo, the Mupulungo of today, the type specimens belong to a population which was temporarily known as the "Lemon-*moori*".

The first data on the colouration in life of a *Tropheus* population was published by POLL in 1956. A more detailed examination of the northwestern shore of Lake Tanganyika by MARLIER (1959) eventually revealed that the genus *Tropheus* is distributed along the shore-zone in numerous isolated populations which usually differ considerably with regard to their colours. In 1962, MATTHES described another five colour morphs. Ichthyological research excursions and the search for new aquarium fishes then resulted in the discovery of a multitude of further colour varieties (STAECK 1974, 1975). The first live specimens were imported into Germany from the northwestern shore (Zaïre) in 1958, but due to inadequate husbandry conditions, these soon disappeared. Beginning in 1971, regular imports from Burundi were observed, followed by exports from Tanzania and Zambia in 1974 and 1975.

Based on the present state of knowledge, the *Tropheus* populations from the immediate vicinity of the town of Mupulungu, the type locality in the southern tip of the lake, are the only ones that can undoubtedly be assigned to the species *Tropheus moorii*. The colour of these fish, which all have a yellow-ish to greyish green ground colour, was first described in the mid-seventies (STAECK 1975).

The most significant colour feature of *Tropheus moorii* is a large lateral blotch which is subject to a high degree of variability with regard to shape and size. In general, it begins right behind the operculum and is, depending on the origin, of lemon-yellow to orange colour. The head of adult specimens is speckled with a multitude of tiny little light dots. Except for a dark zone on the top edge, the iris is bright silver bordered with red. The dorsal fin is blueish grey or blueish in most populations, but may be reddish violet in others.

Young and female specimens are patterned with seven narrow yellowish transversal stripes between the gill-cover and the base of the caudal peduncle.

With increasing age, these stripes gradually fade and remain visible only in the back region. Dominant males completely lack this striped pattern.

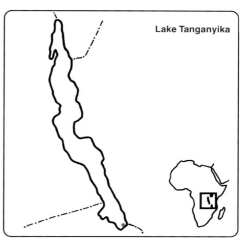

Locality of *Tropheus moorii*

Although *Tropheus moorii* usually reaches just thirteen centimetres in length, its successful long-term

care

requires very spacious aquaria of at least one and a half metres in length. This is due to the

Tropheus moorii from the vicinity of Kalambo

fact that the specimens are highly unsociable and aggressive amongst each other. Under too cramped conditions it will be unavoidable to experience losses. In the long run, it will therefore also be impossible to keep more than one adult male in a tank of ordinary size. This male specimen should be given a harem of at least half a dozen adult females. Within this group, a relatively inflexible rank and pecking order will soon be established in which all members of the group know one another. This obviously becomes a problem when it is undertaken to integrate new specimens into such an aquarium. It requires a great amount of care since there is a high risk that the established *Tropheus* may attack the newcomers and soon kill them. Although it has repeatedly been successful to keep small groups of one male with two females for example — usually in large community aquaria — for a longer period, but these cases must be considered exceptions. It must also be borne in mind that there are considerable individual dif-

ferences in the amount of aggression in different specimens.

When the aquarium is decorated, it should be tried to emulate the rubble- and rocky littoral — as far as is possible. It must not be overlooked that small and very small cracks and cavities are created which can serve the juveniles as sanctuaries and hiding-sites in the beginning.

Although *Tropheus moorii* occasionally nibbles on delicate offshoots of certain plants, it can generally be considered plant-tolerant. Notwithstanding this, the greening of the aquarium should be sparse since it is actually not according to the natural biotope and may narrow the available space for this swift and active swimmer. It is recommendable to use plants only for the upper regions of the rock constructions and therefore choose species which anchor directly on the rocks.

Tropheus moorii is an extremely eager feeder which willingly accepts all common types of food. Ox-heart and earthworms are

The loamy, murky water flowing into Lake Tanganyika in the mouthing areas of the rivers forms a barrier that separates neighbouring *Tropheus* populations and prevents them to mix.

not adequate for this specialized fish. A high danger exists when Red Mosquito larvae and *Tubifex* are fed as these often originate from contaminated water and thus lead to severe diseases. In the early stages an infection can be recognized by an unwillingness to feed which eventually goes over to a total refusal of food.

Very positive experiences were made when this Cichlid was kept in a community aquarium that also accommodates other Tanganyika-cichlids. Adequate co-inhabitants of the tank can be *Tropheus duboisi* or *Tropheus polli,* but also the Goby Cichlids and smaller species of *Julidochromis.* On the other hand, the majority of the species of *Neolamprologus* are unsuitable for living in the company of the vivid and rough *Tropheus* as these require tranquillity and would run the risk of being unable to get enough food in such an aquarium.

If appropriate attention is paid to the aforesaid regarding the husbandry conditions for this Cichlid, the

breeding

is no problem at all. Since *Tropheus moorii* is no predatory fish and does not pursue

Tropheus sp. in their natural habitat; a rubble-zone at two metres depth south of the mouth of the Lufubu (Zambia)

juveniles, the fry can be reared without losses in a naturally decorated tank even in the presence of adult fish. It is nevertheless important that the young fish have a large enough number of suitable sanctuaries available when they leave the mouth of the mother. Because *T. moorii* and *T. duboisi* resemble one another with regard to their sexual and reproductive behaviour, reference is made here to the detailed information given for the latter species.

An urgent appeal must be made not to house the different geographical colour races of this species in the same tank as this could easily result in an unwanted interbreeding.

Although cross-breedings between similar colour varieties are more, and those between less similar morphs less frequent, they are possible in principle. When breeding with such species, it should always be the goal to keep the various varieties pure. A hybridisation would veil the colour differences and lead to unsatisfactory intermediate forms.

The

natural habitat

of *Tropheus moorii* are the shallow zones of the rubble-littoral near the shore. Although individual specimens can also be encountered at much deeper levels, their preferred depths are clearly between one and three metres. Here, the species can sometimes be found in surprisingly dense populations. In contrast to *T. duboisi, T. moorii* is no individualist, but lives in close contact to its conspecifics in the natural setting.

At present, our state of knowledge on the species of *Tropheus* is mainly based upon observations made in the extreme north and south of the lake as well as in northern and central Tanzania. The other parts of the lake are less intensely investigated.

The genus *Tropheus* is not only of special importance for the aquarist, but has also drawn scientific interest. This systematic unit obviously is one of the rare cases where the process of speciation is not completed, but is presently proceeding at full speed.

This fish is distributed along the coastline of its lake in unnumbered populations which are more or less widely separated by geographical barriers. In the course of time a multitude of different features could develop which not only refers to the colouration, but also to ecology, behaviour, morphology, and even anatomy. The extent to which neighbouring populations differ is unequal. In many instances the differences between the individual populations are minor, in others they have been considered so significant that the relevant forms were described as new subspecies or even species.

The fact that the specification is not complete and that the extent to which there are resemblances and differences between populations also cause that new descriptions may not be readily accepted.

An important factor that has led to the development of the great variability of geographical forms is the extreme bonding of the fish to a rocky ground with its typical food resources. Geographical barriers that prevent the contact of neighbouring populations therefore can be coastal areas with sandy ground and river mouths. Having completely adapted to the lawn of algae, *T. moorii* avoid sandy zones because it finds neither food nor hiding-places or suitable breeding sites there. The mouthing areas of large rivers are not inhabited because they are usually swampy and, in contrast to elsewhere in the lake, the water is murky with loam and has a completely different chemical quality.

To date, just under 50 differently coloured populations of *Tropheus* have been described, amongst which there are of course numerous fairly drab forms of less interest to the aquaristic hobby. It should always be borne in mind that there can even be a high degree of colour-variability amongst the individuals of a single population. On several occasions, these formed the basis of marketing "new" varieties in the ornamental fish trade. Several colour morphs have been celebrated as seemingly new discoveries with new names sometimes inadvertently, sometimes consciously fooling the aquarists.

A small selection of the many attractive *Tropheus* populations will be briefly introduced in the following. Until now, not only aquarium literature, but also scientific publications considered the majority of colour morphs as geographical races of *Tropheus moorii*. Today, judging from more recent research, it appears to be clear that this was correct to only a certain extent. Some authors have consolidated various populations to groups assigned to a certain species. In most of these cases the results were rather based upon fairly questionable hypotheses using criteria and methods which do not satisfy scientific requirements (e.g. KONINGS 1988, BRICHARD 1989). The genus *Tropheus* definitely needs to be revised in its entirety.

Since such high-flying attempts appear to be untimely due to the available information, the populations dealt with in the following are identified either by the place of origin or, if such is unknown, by their trade names.

Regular aeroplanes land directly on Lake Tanganyika in the Sumbu National Park. From here, many Cichlids are exported.

◆ *Tropheus* sp.
"Bemba"

The locality of this population lies on the northwestern shore of Lake Tanganyika within the borders of Zaïre. More precisely it lies in the more immediate vicinity of the village of Bemba. Being only a small area, it simultaneously represents the one and only known site where *T. duboisi* occurs outside the borders of Tanzania.

After a detailed examination of the northwestern shore this phenotype was already described by MARLIER in 1959. The fish has a brownish black background colour with a broad orange transversal body belt which is more yellowish orange on the back and more reddish orange on the belly. It usually ranges up onto the dorsal fin. The coloured band is highly variable with regard to width and colour; i. e. it may be very narrow or more than twenty millimetres broad in other specimens. It is deep blood-orange in particularly pretty specimens. The male fish shown in the photograph has an

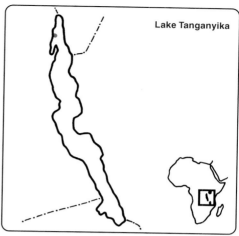

Lake Tanganyika

Locality of *Tropheus* sp. "Bemba"

unusually broad and exceptionally magnificently coloured body-belt.

The first representatives of the genus *Tropheus*, imported into Europe in 1958, belonged to this colour variety. Subsequent imports were not observed before early in 1976.

Tropheus sp. "Bemba"

◆ *Tropheus* sp.
"Rutunga"

Members of this population were imported for the first time in 1971. With a very few exceptions, the aquaristic literature on *Tropheus moorii* published before 1975 actually refers to this colour morph, occasionally also named Brabant-variety. Since it was the only variety kept in aquaria for several years, the name *T. moorii* is often exclusively associated with this phenotype.

The locality of this geographical race lies in the northeastern corner of Lake Tanganyika within the Burundian territory, in the vicinity of the village Rutunga, also named Lutunga on certain maps. Its first description was published by MARLIER in 1959.

The width and colouration of the coloured belt is also highly variable in this form. In most of the cases, it is reduced to an ivory coloured triangle with the apex pointing downwards and a rubyred triangle in the

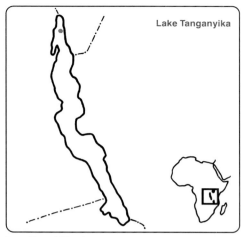

Locality of *Tropheus* sp. "Rutunga"

belly region with the apex pointing upwards. Above the body-belt, the dorsal fin has a ruby-red colourspot. The rest of the body and the fins are pitch black to blackish blue.

Tropheus sp. "Rutunga"

◢ *Tropheus* sp.
"Kigoma"

Fish of this population were caught by me for the first time in spring 1974 and described in the same year. Since autumn 1974 it has also been appearing in the ornamental fish trade. The fish inhabits a very wide range along the northeastern shore of Lake Tanganyika in Tanzania. Its distribution extends from the border areas of Burundi and Tanzania up to the mouth of the Malagarasi River.

Within this vast area, the body colouration of the fish is fairly variable. On a beige-grey, greenish grey, greenish brown, ochrebrown, or pale brown ground, the fish may have seven or eight narrow transversal stripes of beige, golden-yellow, or lemon-yellow colour. A particularly splendid form has lemon-yellow fins.

Amongst the populations of *Tropheus*, this striped variety assumes a certain special position since it is the only one that retains

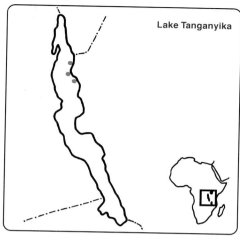

Localities of *Tropheus* sp. "Kigoma"

the approximate juvenile pattern throughout life. Because all other populations of this Cichlid have striped juveniles, it may be assumed that its ancestors also had a striped pattern which might have been similar to the markings of the striped variety.

Tropheus sp. "Kigoma"

◗ *Tropheus* sp.
"Bulu Point"

The exact borders of the area inhabited by this population are presently not yet known. The collecting site is in the vicinity of Bulu Point, a spit of land, south of the village of Magambo in Tanzania. The fish was discovered in autumn 1975 with first imports being observed towards the end of the same year.

The ground colouration of the specimens is anthracite grey to blackish grey. The flanks are marked with two conspicuous blotches whose vertical and horizontal dimensions are as variable as their colour. The anterior blotch is limited to the upper half of the body and extends from about the seventh to the twelfth ray of the dorsal fin whilst the posterior one ranges from the sixteenth to the twentieth ray. The colour of these markings may have any shade from dark ivory to deep reddish orange. The

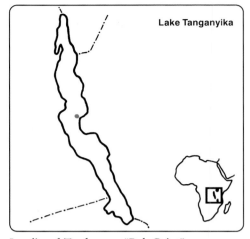

Locality of *Tropheus* sp. "Bulu Point"

upper edge of the iris is always reddish orange.

The biotope is shared with another representative of the genus, namely *Tropheus polli* AXELROD, 1977.

Tropheus sp. "Bulu Point"

◗ *Tropheus* sp.
"Cape Kabeyeye"

This geographical variety was discovered by me in springtime 1975 and described in 1977. Since the initial imports early in 1978, it is often referred to as "Yellow Rainbow" variety.

The distribution of this colour morph extends over the southern part of the Sumbu National Park in Zambia. It occurs from the mouth of the Lufubu near Cape Kabeyeye through Kasaba Bay up to the vicinity of the Kasaba Bay Lodge.

The body of the fish is mainly greenish grey with a large ivory coloured to ochre-yellow blotch in the belly region. In adult specimens, this spot may extend over the entire lower part of the body. The dorsal fin is ivory to greenish beige. The head often assumes a copper-brown tone and is speckled with tiny light dots.

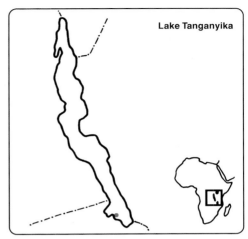

Locality of *Tropheus* sp. "Cape Kabeyeye"

The photograph shows a semi-adult specimen with remainders of the juvenile striped pattern still present.

Tropheus sp. "Cape Kabeyeye"

◆ *Tropheus* sp.
"Cape Kachese"

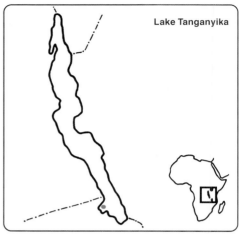

Lake Tanganyika

Locality of *Tropheus* sp. "Cape Kachese"

The natural biotope of this phenotype was discovered by SCHEUERMANN in 1975 and described in the same year. It lies on the northern border of the Sumbu National Park in Zambia, more precisely on Cape Kachese, a spit of land, north of the village of Sumbu.

The upper half of the body of this splendid fish is deep olive green, the lower half is chrome-yellow. The chin and one or two stripes that may mark the forehead, have the same yellow colour. The fins, and the dorsal fin in particular, are yellowish to reddish orange. First imports were observed in 1975.

The orange stripe on the forehead, from which the variety derives its name, is not shown by all individuals. It possibly emerges only during the process of ageing. This variety is very similar to the green and red race from farther south, which lacks both the orange coloured dorsal fin and also a chrome-yellow belly-region.

Tropheus sp. "Cape Kachese"

◆ *Tropheus* sp.
"Chimba"

The natural biotope of this colour morph lies in the southwestern corner of Lake Tanganyika in Zambia. The population is one of those with a very limited range confined to the Cameron Bay, near Chimba.

The "Black and Red" variety was discovered and originally described by German aquarists in 1975. First imports were made in the same year, and subsequently the fish was frequently referred to as "Red Zambian" in the ornamental fish trade.

Under shock, the fish assumes a uniform scarlet or coral-red colouration, whilst under normal circumstances the colour is more or less overlain with black and thus gives it a more oxide-red or brownish red colour. The chin and the interocular region are usually marked with a distinct red stripe.

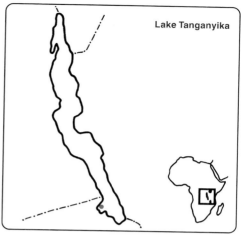

Locality of *Tropheus* sp. "Chimba"

The bases of the pectoral and anal fins are blueish lilac.

Tropheus sp. "Chimba"

▶ *Tropheus* sp.
"Murago"

The discovery of this fish is based on collecting activities by BRICHARD who also was the first to import it into Europe in 1982. These initial imports exclusively consisted of single males which were displayed at exhibitions. Several years had to pass until the fish eventually appeared in the pet shops. During this time, the Cichlid was bred in open-air ponds in Burundi until it became available in numbers sufficient enough to export juveniles.

The precise collecting locality of this species was a matter of guessing for a long time since BRICHARD kept all relevant information secret for commercial purposes until his death (comp. BRICHARD 1989: 179). Today it appears to be certain that it occurs in a small area between the villages of Zongwe and Moba on the west coast (BURNEL, 1993). A greyish green ground colour-

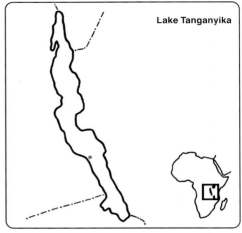

Locality of *Tropheus* sp. "Murago"

ation, narrow yellow transversal stripes, and a conspicuous spotted pattern on the head — distinct only in adult specimens — are typical for this Cichlid.

Tropheus sp. "Murago"

◗ *Tropheus* sp.

"Cape Mpimbwe"

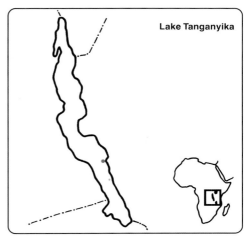

Locality of *Tropheus* sp. "Cape Mpimbwe"

This Cichlid belongs to the representatives of the genus *Tropheus* which were offered by the ornamental fish trade none earlier than the mid-eighties. It originates from the vicinity of the village Luganda (Utinta on older maps) on the central eastern shore in Tanzania. It is also found on Cape Mpimbwe, situated half-way between Kipili in the south and Karema in the north.

The fish has a fairly dark, reddish brown background colouration that covers the body and all fins. Its most peculiar colour characteristic is a deep yellowish orange zone that extends over the lower half of the head from the mouth to the edge of the gill-cover. Furthermore, it has a conspicuous light blue iris whose top third is black. Female specimens, and juveniles in particular, have a pattern of nine narrow, yellowish green, transversal stripes between the edge of the operculum and the base of the tail which only remains visible in the back region of older specimens. Except an orange coloured head, old dominant males are often uniformly reddish brown.

Tropheus sp. "Cape Mpimbwe"

The Genus Xenotilapia

BOULENGER, 1899

This genus, considered part of the tribe Ectodini by POLL (1956), presently contains twelve species, two of which were described only very recently. All of them are small to moderately large fishes with a pronounced head and a fairly slender posterior half of the body. Moreover, the body appears to be distinctly flattened ventrally in most species.

The peculiar trait of this cladistic group is the unusual shape of the ventral fins. Normally, the anterior spines of the ventral fins are the largest, but it is typical for most species of *Xenotilapia* that the posterior ones are the longest. This curious shape of the fins is an adaption to the ecology of these Cichlids which have a habit of resting on the ground for long periods and use the ventrals to support the body. A majority of species of *Xenotilapia* do not live above rocky ground, but in the sandy littoral, so that aquarists rightfully refer to them as Sandcichlids.

▶ Xenotilapia papilio

BÜSCHER, 1990

This Cichlid was discovered and first imported into Europe by BÜSCHER in 1989. On reaching a maximum length of eight to nine centimetres, *Xenotilapia papilio* is one of the smallest representatives this genus has to offer. Since there are no distinct differences in the appearance of males and females, the sex of this Cichlid can only be determined from the different sizes of the urogenital papillae.

Specimens from the type locality have a ground colour resembling the sand which is overlain with three to five narrow light blue longitudinal stripes on the flanks. In its distant spinous portion, the dorsal fin is marked with a broad black longitudinal band above which there is a narrow whitish

submarginal line. The anterior base of this fin has a shade of yellow. The ventral fins are deep lemonyellow, and the anal fin is marked with an alternating pattern of light blue and yellow stripes. The mainly colourless and translucent caudal fin has a black posterior margin. The most dominant colour trait of this fish is a number of small black spots and dots that mark in varying density all fins except the pectorals.

A couple of geographical colour morphs are known from *Xenotilapia papilio* which mainly differ with regard to the content of yellow tones and the shape of black patterns in the fins.

The

natural habitat

of *Xenotilapia papilio* is the lower shore-zone of Lake Tanganyika where BÜSCHER observed the fish at depths between three and forty metres. In contrast to other species of this genus, this Cichlid does not inhabit sandy areas, but zones with large rocks and boulders as well as steep rock faces. According to observations made by its discoverer, adult specimens are strictly territorial and usually live in pairs in fairly large territories. Examinations of stomach contents revealed (BÜSCHER, 1990) that the specimens had mainly fed on infusoria, but occasionally also on small shrimps of the *Cyclops* group and larvae of mosquitos, ephemera, and filamentous algae.

The type locality of *Xenotilapia papilio* lies on the southwestern shore of Lake Tanganyika, forty kilometres south of the town of Moba in Zaïre. Its distribution appears to extend up to the very south of the lake since also Zambia exports Cichlids which obviously belong to this species.

An appropriate

care

will involve a moderately large aquarium with a floor-space of 50×100 centimetres and rocks piled up against the rear wall providing cave-like hiding places. Coarse sand is a recommendable substrate. Suitable company-fishes are found amongst the smaller species of *Julidochromis* and *Neolamprologus,* various shell-dwelling Cichlids, and the representatives of the genera *Cyprichromis* and *Paracyprichromis.*

Breeding

Xenotilapia papilio is a biparental mouthbrooder that also displays a caring behaviour which is comparatively rare amongst Cichlids in general, and also amongst Tanganyika-cichlids. BÜSCHER (1992) reported that the eggs and larvae are cared for in the mouth of the mother during the first six to twelve days after which they are passed on to the male. From the eleventh day on, both parents usually care for the fry simultaneously. Approximately two weeks after spawning the juveniles are released from the mouth for the first time. The mouthbrooding care is then usually continued for another two weeks in co-operation.

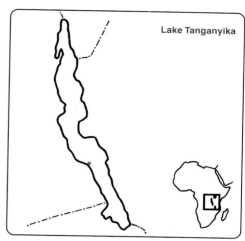

Locality of *Xenotilapia papilio*

It is important to know that *Xenotilapia papilio* differs from many other mouthbrooders in feeding regularly during mouthbrooding and therefore needs to be fed accordingly. It is advisable to offer the fish only small prey-items such as nauplii of *Artemia* during this time.

Xenotilapia papilio

REGISTER OF COMMONLY USED SYNONYMS

Cyprichromis nigripinnis	=	*Paracyprichromis nigripinnis*
Haplochromis borleyi	=	*Copadichromis borleyi*
Haplochromis johnstoni	=	*Placidochromis johnstoni*
Haplochromis labrosus	=	*Placidochromis milomo*
Haplochromis polystigma	=	*Nimbochromis polystigma*
Haplochromis rostratus	=	*Fossorochromis rostratus*
Haplochromis venustus	=	*Fossorochromis venustus*
Haplotaxodon tricoti	=	*Benthochromis tricoti*
Lamprologus boulengeri	=	*Neolamprologus boulengeri*
Lamprologus brevis	=	*Neolamprologus brevis*
Lamprologus brichardi	=	*Neolamprologus brichardi*
Lamprologus callipterus	=	*Neolamprologus callipterus*
Lamprologus compressiceps	=	*Altolamprologus compressiceps*
Lamprologus fasciatus	=	*Neolamprologus fasciatus*
Lamprologus furcifer	=	*Neolamprologus furcifer*
Lamprologus leleupi longior	=	*Neolamprologus longior*
Lamprologus lemairii	=	*Neolamprologus lemairii*
Lamprologus modestus	=	*Neolamprologus modestus*
Lamprologus moorii	=	*Neolamprologus moorii*
Lamprologus nkambae	=	*Lepidiolamprologus nkambae*
Lamprologus savoryi	=	*Neolamprologus savoryi*
Lamprologus sexfasciatus	=	*Neolamprologus sexfasciatus*
Lamprologus signatus	=	*Neolamprologus signatus*
Limnochromis permaxillaris	=	*Gnathochromis permaxillaris*
Ophthalmochromis nasutus	=	*Ophthalmotilapia nasuta*
Sarotherodon mossambicus	=	*Oreochromis mossambicus*

BIBLIOGRAPHY

ALBRECHT, H. (1966): Zur Stammesgeschichte einiger Bewegungsweisen bei Fischen; untersucht am Verhalten von *Haplochromis* — Zeitschr. f. Tierps., 23: 270—302
—— (1968): Freiwasserbeobachtungen an Tilapien in Ostafrika — Zeitschr. f. Tierps., 25: 377—394
——, R. APFELBACH & WICKLER, W. (1968): Über die Eigenständigkeit der Art *Tilapia grahami* BOULENGER, ihren Grubenbau und die Zucht in reinem Süßwasser — Senckenbergiana Biol., 49: 107—118
APFELBACH, R. (1966): Maulbrüten und Paarbindung bei *Tilapia galilaea* — Die Naturwissenschaften, 53: 22
—— (1968): Entwicklung der Brutpflege beim Buntbarsch *Tilapia* — Aquarien-Magazin, 2: 212—213
—— (1969): Vergleichend quantitative Untersuchungen des Fortpflanzungsverhaltens brutpflegemono- und dimorpher Tilapien — Zeitschr. f. Tierps., 26: 692—725
——, D. LEONG (1970): Zum Kampfverhalten in der Gattung *Tilapia* — Zeitschr. f. Tierps., 27: 98—107
ARONSON, L.R. (1949): An Analysis of Reproductive Behavior in the Mouthbreeding Cichlid Fish, *Tilapia macrocephala* (BLEEKER) — Zoologica, 34: 133—158
BAASCH, P. (1987): Maulbrüter mit Elternfamilie: *Limnochromis auritus* — DCG-Inform., 18: 66—71
BAERENDS, G. P. & J.M. BAERENDS-VAN ROON (1950): An Introduction to the Study of the Ethology of Cichlid Fishes — Behaviour, Suppl. 1
BERG, L.S. (1958): System der rezenten und fossilen Fischartigen und Fische — Berlin
BOULENGER, G.A. (1899): A Revision of the African and Syrian Fishes of the Family Cichlidae — Proc. Zool. Soc. London, 1899: 98—143
—— (1915): Catalogue of the Fresh-Water Fishes of Africa in the British Museum of Natural History, 3
—— (1916): Catalogue of the Fresh-Water Fishes of Africa in the British Museum of Natural History, 4
BRESTOWSKY, M. (1968): Vergleichende Untersuchungen zur Elternbindung von *Tilapia*-Jungfischen — Zeitschr. f. Tierps., 25: 761—828
BRICHARD, P. (1975): Réflexions sur le choix de la nidification ou de l'incubation buccale comme mode de reproduction chez certaines populations de Poissons Cichlides de Lac Tanganika — Rev. Zool. Afr., 89: 870—888
—— (1989): Pierre Brichard's Book of Cichlids and all the other Fishes of Lake Tanganyika — Neptune City (T.F.H.), 544 pp.
BURGESS, W.E. (1975): New Developments in the Malawi Genus *Labidochromis* — Trop. Fish. Hobbyist, 24 (Dec.): 44—48
—— (1976): A new *Melanochromis* from Lake Malawi, with Comments of the Genus — Trop. Fish Hobbyist, 24 (Feb.): 61—65
—— (1976): Two new Species of Mbuna (Rock-dwelling Cichlids) from Malawi — Trop. Fish. Hobbyist, 24 (Mar.): 44—52
—— & H.R. AXELROD (1975): *Haplochromis linni*, a new Species of Cichlid from Lake Malawi — Trop. Fish Hobbyist, 23 (Jun.): 36—41
BURNEL, P. (1992): Les *Tropheus* aperçu géographique — Rev. Fr. Cichlidophiles, 127: 7—28
COLOMBÉ, J. (1979): *Pseudotropheus tropheops romandi*, sousespèce nouvelle du Lac Malawi (Pisces, Teleostei, Cichlidae) — Rev. Fr. d'Aquariologie, 6: 33—38
COULTER, G.W. (1967): Low Apparent Oxygen Requirements of Deep-water Fishes in Lake Tanganyika — Nature, 215: 317—318
CRAPON DE CAPRONA, D. (1974): The Effect of Chemical Stimuli from Conspecifics on the Behavior of *Haplochromis burtoni* (Cichlids, Pisces) — Experimentia, 30: 1394—1395
DAGET, J. (1988): Mutanda ichthyologica: *Thysochromis* nom. nov. remplacement de Thysia (Pisces, Cichlidae) — Cybium, 12: 97

DARLINGTON, P.J. (1957): Zoogeography — Cambridge (Harvard Univ.)
DE BEAUFORT, L.F. (1951): Zoogeography of the Land and Inlandwaters London
ECCLES, D.H. (1973): Two new Species of Cichlid Fishes from Lake Malawi — Arnoldia, 6: 1—7
—— & E. TREWAVAS (1989): Malawian Cichlid Fishes: The classification of some Haplochromine genera — Herten (Lake Fish Movies) 335 pp.
EIBL-EIBESFELD, I. (1967): Grundriß der vergleichenden Verhaltensforschung — Munich
FRYER, G. (1956): New Species of Cichlid Fishes from Lake Nyasa — Rev. Zool. Bot. Africaines, 53: 81—91
—— (1959): The Trophic Interrelationships and Ecology of some Littoral Communities of Lake Nyasa with especial Reference to the Fishes, and a Discussion of the Evolution of a Group of Rockfrequenting Cichlidae — Proc. Zool. Soc. London, 132: 153—281
—— & T.D. ILES (1972): The Cichlid Fishes of the Great Lakes of Africa — Edinburgh
GEISLER, R. (1964): Wasserkunde für die aquaristische Praxis — Stuttgart
GOLDSCHMIDT, T. & F. WITTE (1992): Explosive Speciation and Adaptive Radiation of Haplochromine Cichlids from Lake Victoria: An Illustration of the scientific Value of a lost Species Flock — Mitt. Internat. Ver. Limnol., 23: 101—107
GREENBERG, B. (1963): Parental Behaviour and Imprinting in Cichlid Fishes — Behaviour, 21: 127—144
GREENWOOD, P.H. (1956): A Revision of the Lake Victoria *Haplochromis* species (Pisces, Cichlidae), Pts. 1—6 — Bull. Brit. Mus. Nat. Hist. Zool., 4: 233—244; (1957) 5: 76—97; (1959): 5: 179—218; (1960) 6: 227—281; (1962) 9: 139—213; (1967): 15: 29—119
—— (1956): The monotypic Genera of Cichlid Fishes in Lake Victoria — Bull. Brit. Mus. Nat. Hist. Zool., 3: 295—333
—— (1959): The monotypic Genera of Cichlid Fishes in Lake Victoria, Part II — Bull. Brit. Mus. Nat. Hist. Zool., 5: 163—177
—— (1974): The Cichlid Fishes of the Lake Victoria, East Africa: The Biology and Evolution of a Species Flock — Bull. Brit. Mus. Nat. Hist. Zool., Suppl., 6
—— (1979): Towards a Phyletic Classification of the "Genus" *Haplochromis* (Pisces, Cichlidae) and related Taxa, Pts. 1-2 — Bull. Brit. Mus. Nat. Hist. Zool., 35: 265—322; (1980) 39: 1—101
—— (1987): The Genera of Pelmatochromine Fishes (Teleostei, Cichlidae): A phylogenetic Review — Bull. Brit. Mus. Nat. Hist. Zool., 53: 139—203
—— & J.M. GEE (1969): A Revision of the Lake Victoria *Haplochromis* Species (Pisces, Cichlidae), Pt. 7 — Bull. Brit. Mus. Nat. Hist. Zool., 18: 1—65
HEILIGENBERG, W. (1964): Ein Versuch zur ganzheitsbezogenen Analyse des Instinktverhaltens eines Fisches *(Pelmatochromis subocellatus kribensis)* — Zeitschr. f. Tierps., 21: 1—52
HERRMANN, H.-J. (1987): Die Buntbarsche der Alten Welt — Essen (R. Hobbing), 240 pp.
HOLZBERG, S. (1978): A Field and Laboratory Study of the Behaviour and Ecology of *Pseudotropheus zebra* (BOULENGER), an endemic Cichlid of Lake Malawi (Pisces, Cichlidae) — Z. Zool. Syst. Evolutionsf., 16: 171—187
ILES, T.D. (1960): A Group of Zooplankton Feeders of the Genus *Haplochromis* (Cichlidae) in Lake Nyasa — Ann. Mag. Nat. Hist., Ser. 13, 2: 257—280
—— & M.J. HOLDEN (1969): Bi-parental Mouth Brooding in *Tilapia galilaea* — Jour. Zool., 158: 327—333
JACKSON, P. B. N. (1961): Check List of the Fishes of Nyasaland — Occ. Papers National Mus. Southern Rhodesia, Nat. Sci., 25B)
—— et al. (1954): Report on the Survey of Northern Lake Nyasa 1954—1955 — Zomba

JOHNSON, D.S. (1974): New Cichlids from Lake Malawi — Today's Aquarist, 1: 12 — 17
— — (1974): Three new Cichlids from Lake Malawi — Today's Aquarist, 1: 38 — 42
— — (1975): More new Malawi Cichlids — Today's Aquarist, 2: 15 — 18; 20 — 26
— — (1976): Two new Cichlids of the Mbuna Group from Malawi with a Discussion of several Bicuspid-toothed *Labidochromis* sp. — Today's Aquarist, 2: 17 — 24
KASSELMANN, C. (1987): Der Schneckenbuntbarsch *Lamprologus callipterus* im Aquarium: Verhalten — Pflege — Zucht — Aquar. Mag., 21: 328 — 331
KIRCHSHOFER, R. (1953): Aktionssystem des Maulbrüters *Haplochromis desfontanesii* — Zeitschr. f. Tierps., 10: 297 — 318
KLEINBRAHM, W. (1965): Abweichendes Brutverhalten von *Pelmatochromis klugei* — DATZ, 18: 349
KONINGS, A. (1988): Tanganyika Cichlids — Zevenhuisen (Verduijn Cichlids), 271 pp.
— — (1989): Malawi Cichlids in their natural Habitat — Zevenhuisen (Verduijn Cichlids), 303 pp.
KOSSEIG, C. (1965): Genetische Grundlagen des Polymorphismus — Zool. Anz., 175: 21 — 50
KÜHME, W (1962): Das Schwarmverhalten elterngeführter Jungcichliden — Zeitschr. f. Tierps., 19: 513 — 539
— — (1963): Chemisch ausgelöste Brutpflege- und Schwarmreaktionen bei *Hemichromis bimaculatus* — Zeitschr. f. Tierps., 20: 688 — 704
LADIGES, W. (1959): Beiträge zur Kenntnis der Cichliden des Tanganyikasees I — Internat. Rev. gesamt. Hydrobiologie, 44: 431 — 438
LATTIN, G. de (1967): Grundriß der Zoogeographie — Stuttgart
LEYHAUSEN, P. (1949): Kennen Fische sich persönlich — DATZ, 2: 130 — 131
LIEM, K.F. (1981): A phyletic Study of the Lake Tanganyika Cichlid Genera *Asprotilapia, Ectodus, Lestradea, Cunningtonia, Ophthalmochromis* and *Ophthalmotilapia* — Bull. Mus. Comp. Zool. Harvard, 149: 191 — 214
— — & D.J. STEWART (1980): Evolution of the Scale-eating Cichlid Fishes of Tanganyika: A generic Revision — Bull. Mus. Comp. Zool. Harvard, 147: 319 — 350
LINKE, H. (1975): Man nannte sie "*Pelmatochromis*" (I) — Das Aquarium, 9: 431 — 434
— — (1975): Man nannte sie "*Pelmatochromis*" (II) — Das Aquarium, 9: 481 — 484
— — (1976): Man nannte sie "*Pelmatochromis*" (III) — Das Aquarium, 10: 10 — 15
— — (1977): Man nannte sie "*Pelmatochromis*". Die Gattung *Nanochromis* — Das Aquarium, 11: 111 — 114
— — (1976): *Chromidotilapia guentheri* — ein Maulbrüter aus Westafrika — Tatsachen und Informationen aus der Aquaristik, 10: 10 — 11
— — (1978): Man nannte sie *Pelmatochromis. Pelvicachromis spec. affin. pulcher,* früher *camerunensis* — Das Aquarium, 12: 11
— — (1978): Die Prachtbuntbarsche Westafrikas: Formen von *Pelvicachromis taeniatus* — Tatsachen und Informationen aus der Aquaristik, 12: 4 — 7
— — (1979): Man nannte sie *Pelmatochromis*. Die dritte Farbpopulation des Buntbarsches *Chromidotilapia finleyi* — Das Aquarium, 13: 391 — 393
— — (1980): Hurra, der "*dimidiatus*" ist wieder da — Das Aquarium, 14: 567 — 569
LOISELLE, P.V. (1979): A Revision of the Genus *Hemichromis* PETERS 1858 (Teleostei: Cichlidae) — Ann. Mus. Royal Afrique centrale, Sci. Zool., No. 228:
— — & R.L. WELCOMME (1972): Description of a new Genus of Cichlid Fish from West Africa — Rev. Zool. Bot. Afr., 85: 37 — 57
LOWE, R.H. (1959): Breeding Behaviour Patterns and Ecological Differences between *Tilapia* Species and their Significance for Evolution within the Genus *Tilapia* — Proc. Zool. Soc. London, 132: 1 — 30
— — (1956): The Breeding Behaviour of *Tilapia* Species in Natural Waters: Observation on *T. karomo* POLL and *T. variabilis* BOULENGER — Behaviour, 9: 140 — 163
MARLER, P. R. & W.J. HAMILTON (1972): Tierisches Verhalten — Minden, Bern, Vienna

MARLIER, G. (1959): Observations sur la biologie littorale du lac Tanganika — Rev. Zool. Bot. Africa, 59: 164 — 183
— — & N. LELEUP (1954): A Curious Ecological "Niche" among the Fishes of Lake Tanganyika — Nature, 174: 935 — 936
MATTHES, H. (1962): Poissons nouveaux ou interessants du lac Tanganika et du Ruanda — Ann. Mus. Roy. Afrique Cent. Sci. Zool., 111: 27 — 88
— — (1959): Un Cichlide nouveau du lac Tanganika: *Julidochromis transcriptus* n. sp. — Rev. Zool. Bot. Africa, 60: 126 — 130
— — (1960): Les communautés écologiques des poissons cichlidae au Lac Tanganika — Folia Sci. Africa Centr., 6: 8 — 12
— — (1962): L'exploration sous-lacustre de lac Tanganika — Africa, Tervuren, 8: 1 — 11
MEYER, A. et al. (1990): Monophyletic origin of Lake Victoria cichlid fishes suggested by mitochondrial DNA sequences — Nature, 347: 550 — 553
MEYER, M.K., R. RIEHL & H. ZETZSCHE (1987): A revision of the cichlid fishes of the genus *Aulonocara* REGAN, 1922 from Lake Malawi, with descriptions of six new species — Cour. Forsch.-Inst. Senckenb., 94: 7 — 53
MYRBERG, A.A. (1964): An Analysis of Preferential Care of Eggs and Young by Adult Cichlid Fishes — Zeitschr. f. Tierps., 21: 53 — 98
— — (1965): A Descriptive Analysis of the Behaviour of the African Cichlid Fish, *Pelmatochromis guentheri* (SAUVAGE) — Animal Behaviour, 13: 312 — 329
— — (1965): Sound Production by Cichlid Fishes — Science, 149: 555 — 558
NEIL, E.H. (1966): Observation on the Behavior of *Tilapia mossambica* (Pisces, Cichlidae) in Hawaiian Ponds — Copeia, 1966: 50 — 56
NELISSEN, M. (1975): Contribution to the Ethology of *Simochromis diagramma* (GÜNTHER). (Pisces, Cichlidae) — Acta Zool. Path. Antv., 61: 19 — 24
— — (1975): Sexual Behaviour in *Simochromis diagramma* (GÜNTHER) (Pisces, Cichlidae) — Acta Zool. Path. Antv., 62: 203 — 206
— — (1976): Contribution to the Ethology of *Tropheus moorei* BOULENGER (Pisces, Cichlidae) and a Discussion of the Significance of its Colour Patterns — Rev. Zool. Africa, 90: 17 — 29
NELISSEN, M. & D. THYS VAN DEN AUDENAERDE (1975): Description of *Tropheus brichardi* sp. nov. from Lake Tanganyika (Pisces, Cichlidae) — Rev. Zool. Africa, 89: 974 — 980
NOBLE, G. K. & B. CURTIS (1939): The Social Behavior of the Jewel Fish, *Hemichromis bimaculatus* — Bull. Amer. Mus. Nat. Hist., 76: 1 — 46
OEHLERT, B. (1958): Kampf und Paarbildung einiger Cichliden — Zeitschr. f. Tierps., 15: 141 — 174
OHM, D. (1959): Das Sozialverhalten von Fischen — Aquarien und Terrarien, 6: 229 — 233
— — (1964): Die Entwicklung des Kommentkampfs bei Jungcichliden — Zeitschr. f. Tierps., 21: 308 — 325
OLIVER, M.K. (1974): *Labidochromis textilis,* a New Cichlid Fish (Teleostei: Cichlidae) from Lake Malawi — Proc. Biol. Soc. Washington, 88: 319 — 330
— — & Y. LOISELLE (1972): A New Genus and Species of Cichlid of the Mbuna Group from Lake Malawi — Rev. Zool. Bot. Africa, 85: 309 — 320
PAULO, J. (1974): Zum Brutpflegeverhalten einer *Chromidotilapia* aus Südkamerun — DATZ, 27: 400 — 402
— — (1979): Eine neue *Chromidotilapia*-Art aus dem Bosumtwe-See/Ghana: *Chromidotilapia bosumtwensis,* species nova (Pisces, Perciformis, Cichlidae) — DCG-Inform., 10: 167 — 174
PELLEGRIN, J. (1904): Contribution à l'étude anatomique, biologique, et taxonomique des poissons de la famille des Cichlides — Mém. Soc. Zool. France, 16: 41 — 402
— — (1929): Silurides, Cyprinodontidés, Acanthoptérygiens du Cameroun recueillis par M.Th. MONOD. Description de cinq espèces et de deux variétés nouvelles — Bull. Soc. Zool. France, 14: 358 — 369
PETERS, H.M. (1937): Experimentelle Untersuchungen über die Brutpflege von *Haplochromis multicolor,* einem maul-

brütenden Knochenfisch — Zeitschr. f. Tierps., 1: 201 — 218

— — (1948): Grundlagen der Tierpsychologie — Stuttgart

— — (1965): Angeborenes Verhalten bei Buntbarschen — Umschau, 65: 665 — 669, 711 — 717

POLL, M. (1939): Les Poissons du Stanley-Pool — Ann. Mus. Congo Belge Zool., Ser. 1, 4 (1): 1 — 60

— — (1946): Révision de la faune ichthyologique du lac Tanganika — Ann. Mus. Congo Belge Zool., Ser. 1, 4 (3): 141 — 364

— — (1950): Histoire du peuplement et origine des espèces de la faune ichthyologique du lac Tanganika — Ann. Soc. Roy. Zool. Belgique, 81: 111 — 140

— — (1956): Poissons Cichlidae — Rés. Sci. Explor. Hydrobiol. Tanganika 1946-1947, Sér. 5B, 3: 1 — 619

— — (1956): Ecologie des poissons du lac Tanganika — XIV. Internat. Congress Zool. 1953: 465 — 468

— — (1957): Les genres des poissons d'eau douce de l'Afrique — Ann. Mus. Roy. Congo Belge Sci. Zool., 54: 1 — 191

— — (1959): Recherches sur la faune ichthyologique de la région du Stanley Pool — Ann. Mus. Roy. Congo Belge Sci. Zool., 71: 75 — 174

— — (1974): Contribution à la faune ichthyologique du lac Tanganika, d'après des récoltes de P. BRICHARD — Rev. Zool. Bot. Africa, 88: 99 — 110

— — (1978): Contribution à la connaissance du genre Lamprologus SCHTH — Bull. Class. Sci. Acad. Roy. Belgique, Ser. 5, 64: 725 — 758

— — (1980): Ethologie comparée des poissons fluviatiles et lacustres africains — Bull. Class. Sci. Acad. Roy. Belgique, Ser. 5, 66: 78 — 97

— — (1986): Classification des Cichlidae du lac Tanganika: Tribus, genres et espèces — Mém. Class. Sci., Sér. XLV, 2: 1 — 163

— — & H. MATTHES (1962): Trois poissons remarquables du lac Tanganika — Ann. Mus. Roy. Africa Cent. Sci. Zool., 111: 1 — 26

— — & D.J. STEWART (1975): A New Cichlid Fish of the Genus Xenotilapia from Lake Tanganyika, Zambia (Pisces, Cichlidae) — Rev. Zool. Bot. Africa, 89: 919 — 924

— — & D. Thys VAN DEN AUDENAERDE (1974): Genre nouveau Triglachromis proposé pour Limnochromis otostigma REGAN, Cichlidae du lac Tanganika — Rev. Zool. Bot. Africa, 88: 127 — 130

REGAN, C.T. (1920): The Classification of the Fishes of the Family Cichlidae, I. The Tanganyika Genera — Ann. Mag. Nat. Hist., Ser. 9, 5: 33 — 53

— — (1921): The Cichlid Fishes of Lake Nyasa — Proc. Zool. Soc. London, 1921: 675 — 727

— — (1921): The Cichlid Fishes of Lakes Albert, Edward and Kivu — Ann. Mag. Nat. Hist., Ser. 9, 8: 632 — 639

— — (1922): The Classification of the Fishes of the Family Cichlidae, II. On African and Syrian Genera not Restricted to the Great Lakes — Ann. Mag. Nat. Hist., Ser. 9, 10: 249 — 264

— — (1922): The Cichlid Fishes of Lake Victoria — Proc. Zool. Soc. London, 1922: 157 — 191

REISINGER, E. (1965): Phänomene und Probleme des Polymorphismus — Zool. Anz., 175: 1 — 20

RIBBINK, A.J., A.C. MARSH, RIBBINK, A.C. & B.J. SHARP (1983): A preliminary survey of the cichlid fishes of rocky habitats in Lake Malawi — S. African Jour. Zool., 18: 147 — 308

ROBERTS, T. R. & D.J. STEWART (1976): An ecological and systematic survey of fishes in the rapids of the lower Zaire or Congo River — Bull. Mus. Comp. Zool. Harvard, 147: 239 — 317

ROMAN, B. (1971): Peces de Rio Muni, Guinea Ecuatorial, Estaciòn de Investigaciones Marinas de Margarita — Venezuela

RUWET, J.-C. & J. VOSS (1966): L'étude des mouvements d'expression chez les Tilapia (Poissons Cichlide) — Bull. Soc. Sci. Liege, 35: 778 — 800

SCHEUERMANN, H. (1977): A partial revision of the Genus Limnochromis REGAN 1920 — Cichlidae, 3: 67 — 73

SCHRÖDER, J.H. (1980): Morphological and behavioural differences between the BB/OB and B/W colour morphs of

Pseudotropheus zebra BOULENGER (Pisces; Cichlidae) — Zeitschr. Zool. Syst. Evolut. Forsch., 18: 69 — 76

SEITZ, A. (1940/41): Die Paarbildung bei einigen Cichliden. I. Die Paarbildung bei Astatotilapia strigigena PFEFFER — Zeitschr. f. Tierps., 4: 40 — 84

— — (1943): Die Paarbildung bei einigen Cichliden. II. Die Paarbildung bei Hemichromis bimaculatus GILL — Zeitschr. f. Tierps., 5: 74 — 101

— — (1949): Vergleichende Verhaltensstudien an Buntbarschen — Zeitschr. f. Tierps., 6: 202 — 235

SHAW, E. S. & L.R. ARONSON (1954): Oral Incubation in Tilapia macrocephala — Bull. Amer. Mus. Nat. Hist., 103: 397 — 415

SPREINAT, A. (1989): Kaiserbuntbarsche des Malawisees — Stuttgart (Ulmer), 106 pp

STAECK, W. (1972): Variabler Pseudotropheus zebra — Das Aquarium, 6: 1051 — 1054

— — (1973): Territorialverhalten bei Aquarienfischen — Das Aquarium, 7: 275 — 279

— — (1974): Balz, Paarung und Brutpflege des Maulbrüters Pseudotropheus elongatus — Das Aquarium, 8: 2 — 6

— — (1974): Biotope und Lebensbedingungen im Tanganjikasee — Das Aquarium, 8: 292 — 297

— — (1974): Tropheus duboisi im Tanganjikasee beobachtet und fotografiert — Das Aquarium, 8: 380 — 383

— — (1974): Eine neue geographische Rasse des Brabantbuntbarsches — Aquarien-Magazin, 8: 504 — 509

— — (1975): Cichliden: Verbreitung, Verhalten, Arten, 1. — Ed. 2, Wuppertal, (Engelbert-Pfriem-Verl.)

— — (1975): Scale-Eaters and Fin-Biters of the East African Lakes — Aquarists and Pondkeeper, 39: 414 — 415, 417

— — (1975): Verschiedener als Schwarz und Weiß: Sexualdimorphismus, Polymorphismus und die Bildung geographischer Rassen bei ostafrikanischen Buntbarschen — Aquarien-Magazin, 9: 124 — 131

— — (1975): Die Grundelbuntbarsche des Tanganjikasees — Aquarien-Magazin, 9: 140 — 147

— — (1975): Eine ausgefallene Ernährungsweise: Schuppenfressende Cichliden — Das Aquarium, 9: 291 — 294

— — (1975): Beobachtungen zum Fortpflanzungs- und Brutpflegeverhalten von Tropheus duboisi — Tatsachen und Informationen aus der Aquaristik, 9: 10 — 11

— — (1975): A New Fish from Lake Tanganyika. Julidochromis dickfeldi sp. n. (Pisces, Cichlidae) — Rev. Zool. Bot. Africa, 89: 982 — 986

— — (1975): Unterwasserbeobachtungen an Lamprologus tetracanthus BOULENGER, 1899 — Tatsachen und Informationen aus der Aquaristik, 9 (32): 26 — 27

— — (1975): Als duboisi-Fänger in Kigoma — Aquarien-Magazin, 9: 470 — 477

— — (1975): Die südlichen Rassen von Tropheus mooreii — Aquarien-Magazin, 9: 518 — 521

— — (1976): Schlankcichliden, Bewohner der Geröll- und Felsenregion: Neue Erkenntnisse über die Gattung Julidochromis — Aquarien-Magazin, 10: 74 — 79

— — (1976): Die Lebensräume im Tanganjikasee — Aquarien-Magazin, 10: 356 — 364

— — (1976): Haplochromis-Arten aus dem Malawisee: Im natürlichen Lebensraum und im Aquarium beobachtet — Aquarien-Magazin, 10: 356 — 364

— — (1976): Ergebnisse einer ichthyologischen Sammelreise zum Nordende des Nyassasees — Das Aquarium, 10: 436 — 442, 486 — 492

— — (1977): Cichliden: Verbreitung, Verhalten, Arten, 2. — Wuppertal (Engelbert-Pfriem-Verlag)

— — (1978): Raritäten aus dem Malawisee: Neuere Erkenntnisse über die Vielgestaltigkeit bei Mbuna-Cichliden — Aquarien-Magazin, 12: 136 — 141

— — (1978): Ein neuer Cichlide aus dem südlichen Tanganjikasee: Lamprologus nkambae n. sp. (Pisces, Cichlidae) — Rev. Zool. Bot. Africa, 92: 436 — 441

— — (1979): Beobachtungen an Kärpflingscichliden: Zur Fortpflanzungsbiologie und Ökologie der Cyprichromis-Arten — Aquarien-Magazin, 13: 99 — 104

— — (1979): Chromidotilapia linkei n. sp. aus dem Mungo River, Kamerun (Pisces: Cichlidae) — Senckenbergiana Biol., 60: 153 — 157

—— (1979): *Pseudotropheus heteropictus* n. sp. aus dem Malawisee (Pisces: Cichlidae) — Senckenbergiana Biol., 60: 159 — 162

—— (1980): Aufwuchsfresser: Beobachtungen an ostafrikanischen Cichliden — Aquarien-Magazin, 14: 43 — 51

—— (1980): Ein neuer Cichlide vom Ostufer des Tanganjikasees: *Lamprologus leleupi longior* n. ssp. (Pisces, Cichlidae) — Rev. Zool. Bot. Africa, 94: 11 — 14

—— (1985): Cichliden: Tanganjika-See — Wuppertal (Engelbert-Pfriem-Verlag), 124 pp

—— (1987): Ein ungewöhnlicher Schneckencichlide: *Lamprologus callipterus* — Aquarien-Magazin, 21: 324 — 327

—— (1988): Zur Synonymie von *Lamprologus kiritvaithai* MEYER et al. 1986 mit *Neolamprologus boulengeri* (STEINDACHNER 1909) — DATZ, 41: 104 — 108

—— (1988): Kaiserbuntbarsche: Gattung *Aulonocara* REGAN, 1922 — DATZ, 41: 224 — 228, 296 — 299

—— (1988): Cichliden: Malawi-See — Wuppertal (Engelbert-Pfriem-Verlag), 147 pp

STERBA, G. (1970): Süßwasserfische aus aller Welt — Melsungen, Berlin, Basel, Wien

STOCK, A.D. (1976): The taxonomic Status of *Labidochromis joanjohnsonae* JOHNSON, *Labidochromis fryeri* OLIVER and *Melanochromis exasperatus* BURGESS — Buntb. Bull., 55: 14 — 19

STURMBAUER, C. & A. MEYER (1992): Genetic divergence, speciation and morphological stasis in a lineage of African cichlid fishes — Nature, 358: 578 — 581

THYS VAN DEN AUDENAERDE, D. (1968): A Preliminary Contribution to a Systematic Revision of the Genus *Pelmatochromis* HUBRECHT sensu lato — Rev. Zool. Bot. Africa, 77: 349 — 391

—— (1968): An Annotated Bibliography of *Tilapia* (Pisces, Cichlidae) — Docum. Zool. Mus. Roy. Afrique Cent., Tervuren, 14:

—— (1968): Description of a new *Pelmatochromis* (Pisces Cichlidae) from Sierra Leone — Rev. Zool. Bot. Africa, 77: 335 — 345

—— (1968): Description of *Tilapia cessiana* sp. nov. with some remarks on *Tilapia (Herotilapia) buttikoferi* (HUBRECHT 1881), (Pisces, Cichlidae) — Rev. Zool. Bot. Africa, 78: 183 — 195

—— & P. LOISELLE (1971): Description of Two New Small African Cichlids — Rev. Zool. Bot. Africa, 83: 193 — 206

TREWAVAS, E. (1935): A synopsis of the Cichlid Fishes of Lake Nyasa — Ann. Mag. Nat. Hist., Ser. 10, 16: 65 — 118

—— (1962): Fishes of the Crater Lakes of the Northwestern Cameroons Bonn. — Zool. Beitr., 13: 146 — 192

—— (1947): An Example of "Mimicry" in Fishes — Nature, 160: 120

—— (1973): On the Cichlid Fishes of the Genus *Pelmatochromis* with Proposal of a New Genus for *Pelmatochromis congicus*; on the Relationships between *Pelmatochromis* and *Tilapia* and the Recognition of *Sarotherodon* as a Distinct Genus — Bull. Brit. Mus. Nat. Hist. Zool., 25: 1 — 26

—— (1969): Description of a small new *Tilapia* (Pisces, Cichlidae) from Sierra Leone — Rev. Zool. Bot. Africa, 80: 157 — 165

—— (1973): A New Species of Cichlid Fishes of Rivers Quanza and Bengo, Angola, with a List of the Known Cichlids of these Rivers and a Note on *Pseudocrenilabrus natalensis* — Bull. Brit. Mus. Nat. Hist. Zool., 25: 27 — 37

—— (1974): The Freshwater Fishes of Rivers Mungo and Meme and Lakes Kotto, Mboandong and Soden, West Cameroon — Bull. Brit. Mus. Nat. Hist. Zool., 26: 393 — 397

—— (1975): A new species of *Nanochromis* (Pisces, Cichlidae) from the Ogowe System, Gabon — Bull. Brit. Mus. Nat. Hist. Zool., 28: 233 — 235

—— (1984): Nouvel examen des genres et sous-genres du complexe *Pseudotropheus-Melanochromis* du lac Malawi (Pisces, Perciformes, Cichlidae) — Rev. Fr. Aquariol., 10: 97 — 106

VOSS, J. (1969): Contribution à l'éthologie des poissons Cichlides: *Tilapia zillii* GERVAIS, 1848) — Rev. Zool. Bot. Africa, 79: 99 — 109

—— (1969): Contribution à l'éthologie des poissons Cichlides: *Pelmatochromis ansorgii* (BOULENGER, 1901) — Acta Zool. Pathol. Antv., 50: 29 — 43

—— (1970): Contribution à l'éthologie des poissons Cichlides: *Tilapia sparrmanii* SMITH, 1840 — Rev. Zool. Bot. Africa, 85: 369 — 388

—— & J.-C. RUWET (1966): Inventaire des mouvements d'expression chez *Tilapia guineensis* (BLKR., 1863) et *T. macrochir* (BLGR., 1912). (Poissons Cichlides) — Ann. Soc. Roy. Zool. Belgique, 96: 145 — 188

WICKLER, W. (1958): Vergleichende Verhaltensstudien an Grundfischen II. Die Spezialisierung des *Steatocranus* — Zeitschr. f. Tierps., 15: 427 — 446

—— (1959): *Teleogramma brichardi* POLL 1959 — DATZ, 12: 228 — 230

—— (1962): Ei-Attrappen und Maulbrüten bei afrikanischen Cichliden — Zeitschr. f. Tierps., 18: 129 — 164

—— (1963): Zur Klassifikation der Cichlidae, am Beispiel der Gattungen *Tropheus, Petrochromis, Haplochromis* und *Hemihaplochromis* n. gen. — Senckenbergiana Biol., 44: 83 — 96

—— (1965): Die Evolution von Mustern der Zeichnung und des Verhaltens — Die Naturwiss., 52: 335 — 341

—— (1966): Ein augenfressender Buntbarsch — Natur und Museum, 96: 311 — 315

—— (1966): Sexualdimorphismus, Paarbildung und Versteckbrüten — Zool. Jahrb. Syst., 93: 127 — 138

—— (1966): Über die biologische Bedeutung des Genitalanhangs der männlichen *Tilapia macrochir* — Senckenbergiana Biol., 47: 419 — 427

—— (1969): Zur Soziologie des Brabantbuntbarsches, *Tropheus moorei* — Zeitschr. f. Tierps., 26: 967 — 987

WILHELM, W. (1980): The Disputed Feeding Behaviour of a Paedophagus Haplochromine Cichlid (Pisces) Observed and Discussed — Behaviour, 74: 310 — 323

PHOTO CREDITS

All photographs by Wolfgang STAECK, with exception
of those on pages
13, 55, 62, 93, 103, 107, 125, 126, 139 (Horst LINKE);
52 (Erwin SCHRAML);
54 (Lothar SEEGERS).

THE AUTHORS

Wolfgang STAECK, born 1939, studied biology and English literature at the Free University Berlin, Germany. After his State Diploma he worked as an associate researcher at the Technical University Berlin for several years. In the year 1972 he conferred a degree with the minor subjects Zoology and Botany.

Dr. STAECK is known to a wide public through numerous lectures and the publication of books and papers in journals. Since 1966 he has published a vast number of contributions on Cichlids in German and foreign magazines. Since his major interest is focused on behavioural studies in Cichlids, he is still an aquarist today and familiar with the maintenance and breeding of Cichlids with the experience of many years.

During his numerous study-trips which were primarily intended to learn more about Cichlids in their natural environments and resulted in the discoveries of many new species, subspecies, and colour varieties, he travelled East Africa especially, but also West Africa and Madagascar. In recent times he undertook journeys to Central and South America to study and collect Cichlids in Mexico, Brazil, Ecuador, Venezuela, Peru, and Bolivia.

A high priority of his research was spent on the Cichlids of the Lakes Malawi and Tanganyika. Not only in these waters but also in rivers of Central and South America, he observed and took photographs of the world of fishes as a diver. Through this he managed to document the ecology and the inhabited biotopes of many Cichlids for the very first time in underwater photographs. As a result of his study-trips he published scientific descriptions of several new species of Cichlids.

Horst LINKE, born in 1938, has had an interest in the aquarium since early childhood. Already quite early the dream of all enthusiastic aquarists to visit the tropical habitats of our aquarium-fishes came true for him. In the year 1963 he undertook a journey throughout Black Africa, and two years later he had opportunity to visit the countries of Panama, Venezuela, Peru, and Bolivia. From the contacts with the aquarium-fishes in the wild, new questions and tasks always developed so that he visited some countries not only once but repeatedly. Beginning in 1973, he undertook collecting and study expeditions to Cameroon, Nigeria, Ghana, Togo, Sierra Leone, Tanzania, Kenya, Thailand, Sumatra, Borneo, Malaysia, Colombia, Peru, and Bolivia in quick succession. During his numerous stays abroad it was always of special interest for him to collect as much information as possible about the life-conditions in the natural biotopes in order to create an optimal environment for the fishes in the aquarium at home. Over the years, his journeys were planned with more and more precisely defined tasks and specific study-goals, may it be to verify doubtful distribution records or to collect material for the work on taxonomical problems.

He made other aquarists profiting from his experiences by lectures, but especially by publications in both national and international periodicals.